A Guide to Better Hatching

Written by
Janet Stromberg

Edited by
Loyl Stromberg

Published by
STROMBERG PUBLISHING COMPANY
Fort Dodge, Iowa   Pine River, Minnesota

Published in the United States by Stromberg Publishing Company,
Fort Dodge, Iowa 50501

Library of Congress Catalog Card Number: 75-14654
International Standard Book Number: 0-915780-00-3

Special Thanks

We wish to extend these few words of appreciation for the valuable assistance and advice given us in the preparation of A Guide to Better Hatching. The following have made it possible to expedite the writing and preparation of this book. They have also added to it considerably with their experience and authorative knowledge on the subject of poultry science. Their help is gratefully appreciated.

Dr. William Cawley
Texas A & M University

Professor John Skinner
University of Wisconsin

Dr. Charles J. Wabeck
University of Maryland

OTHER BOOKS PUBLISHED BY STROMBERG PUBLISHING COMPANY

Successful Duck & Goose Raising

Exhibiting Poultry to Win

Making Squab Raising Profitable

Guinea Fowl

HELPFUL BULLETINS PUBLISHED

Beginners Falconry
Pet Store Opportunities
How & Where to Sell Puppies & Kittens
How to De-Scent Skunk Kittens & Sell Them
How & Where to Sell Small Animals—Rabbits, Guinea Pigs, Gerbils, Hamsters
How & Where to Sell Pigeons
Teaching Crows & Magpies to Talk
Pea Fowl (Peacocks)
Canadian Honkers
Swans—their Care & Breeding

A new book in the future . . .

ENCYCLOPEDIA — POULTRY OF THE WORLD
Research is under way for this exceptional book.
To be exceptionally well illustrated. A book
to look forward to — to add to your library.

also

Caponizing, Management & Profitable Marketing

CONTENTS

R E A P . . . as ye S O W

    This is a very fitting statement concerning successful hatches. By nature, all fowl will reproduce. Good management will result in better hatches!

INTRODUCTION

There are numerous factors affecting the successful hatching and raising of all fowl. The chain of events begins long before the eggs are set or placed in the incubator. Our modern science and technology has provided us with a great deal of information on this subject.

Each species of fowl has its own peculiarities that should be understood. Basically, we must consider the parent stock, their nutrition, and their environment. We must study all the factors leading up to the laying of a fertile egg.

Once the egg is produced, great care should be taken to insure that the egg to chick cycle runs its full course. We know that there are certain types of eggs that hatch better than others. The hatching eggs must be stored and cared for properly.

Finally, the egg must be incubated properly in order to hatch. There are many styles of incubators that will perform the function of hatching fowl successfully. Care for the egg does not end when the egg is placed in the incubator, but must be continued throughout the incubation period. The whole idea of incubation is to turn an egg into a strong healthy chick. This means we must have a fertile egg from a healthy, well fed, hen and the proper equipment to provide temperature, exercise (turning), humidity, and ventilation for the egg during the transition from egg to chick.

STRUCTURE OF THE EGG

First, let's briefly study the egg, its makeup, and formation of the chick. When anyone speaks of eggs and incubation they are usually referring to chicken eggs, as they are the ones to which the principles of artificial incubation are commonly applied. There has been less research done on pre-incubation care and incubation of gamebird eggs. Techniques discussed in this book are geared to the poultryman, but most of the concepts can be used by gamebird raisers.

The egg is nature's way of reproducing the species. It must contain all the essential nutrients required to support life. All of these nutrients must be stored in the yolk and albumen of the egg before it is laid. This points out the need for a properly balanced breeder ration in the production of hatching eggs. There are specific differences, however, in nutrient requirements and utilization.

Basically, a successful hatching egg must contain protein, carbohydrates, minerals, vitamins, fats, and water. A deficiency in any one of these essential nutrients will reduce hatchability.

The female cell, the ova, is perhaps the largest cell known. The male cell is microscopic and can't be seen with the naked eye. A fertile egg can't be distinguished from an infertile egg unless the yolk is broken out or until it has been incubated a sufficient length of time to cause development.

The nucleus of the female cell is a small light or white speck about the size of the head of a pin. It's located on the top side of the yolk and is the place where the microscopic male sperm cell finds lodgment and the cells are united to form the embryo.

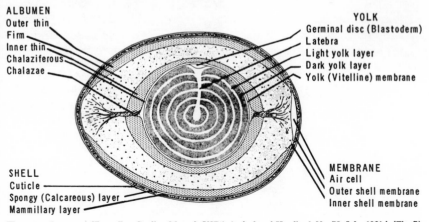

ALBUMEN
Outer thin
Firm
Inner thin
Chalaziferous
Chalazae

YOLK
Germinal disc (Blastoderm)
Latebra
Light yolk layer
Dark yolk layer
Yolk (Vitelline) membrane

MEMBRANE
Air cell
Outer shell membrane
Inner shell membrane

SHELL
Cuticle
Spongy (Calcareous) layer
Mammillary layer

The parts of an egg. (From Egg Grading Manual, USDA Agricultural Handbook No. 75, July, 1961.) (Fig. 7)

FORMATION OF THE EGG

The egg is a delicate organism and it is assembled in a precise order. First, the yolk and ovum are produced. They develop in the ovary, a grape-like cluster of ovules or miniature yolks located in the back of the hen. The yolk remains in the ovaries until it is ripe. When it is mature, the yolk drops into the funnel section (infundibulum) of the oviduct. Here the ovum is fertilized by the male sperm cell. As the egg passes to the magnum, a thin layer of albumen (egg white) is placed around the yolk in the form of a thin sack. At either end of the yolk, thin strands of albumen are twisted to form the chalaza. The function of the chalaza cord is to hold the yolk in place as it travels the length of the oviduct, and to prevent it from rising and bruising itself on the shell membranes. It was once thought the chalaza affected the fertility of the egg — this is not so. Its sole purpose is to hold the yolk in the proper position. Before the yolk leaves the magnum the majority of the albumen is wrapped around the yolk. The egg then enters the isthmus where two shell membranes grow around the yolk and albumen. These membranes are loose fitting at this point. Final egg development occurs in the uterus. Actually, about 80% of the time it takes to form an egg is spent in the uterus. The uterus is often referred to as the shell gland for here the inner shell membrane is made tight and the outer, harder shell is produced. The egg moves through the vagina to the cloaca and is finally expelled. The whole egg formation process takes a little more than 24 hours.

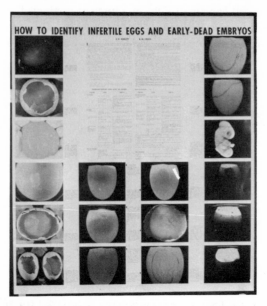

HOW TO IDENTIFY INFERTILE EGGS AND EARLY-DEAD EMBRYOS

This excellent chart in color is available from the University of California, Agricultural Publications Department, Berkley, California. Also, available from Stromberg Pets Unlimited, Fort Dodge, Iowa 50501

EMBRYONIC DEVELOPMENT

Fertilization
Division and growth of living cells
Segregation of cells into groups of special function (tissues)

No growth; stage of inactive embryonic life

——— First sign of resemblance to a chick embryo
——— Appearance of alimentary tract
——— Appearance of vertebral column
——— Beginning of formation of nervous system
——— Beginning of formation of head
——— Beginning of formation of eye

——— Beginning of formation of heart
——— Beginning of formation of ear
——— Heart begins to beat

——— Beginning of formation of nose
——— Beginning of formation of legs
——— Beginning of formation of wings

——— Beginning of formation of tongue

——— Formation of reproductive organs and differentiation of sex

——— Beginning of formation of beak

——— Beginning of formation of feathers

——— Beginning of hardening of beak

——— Appearance of scales and claws

——— Embryo gets position suitable for breaking the shell

——— Scales, claws, and beak becoming firm and horny

——— Beak turns toward air cell

——— Yolk sac begins to enter body cavity

——— Yolk sac completely drawn into body cavity
——— Embryo occupies practically all the space within the egg except the air cell

——— Hatching of chick

DAILY CHANGES IN WEIGHT AND FORM OF THE DEVELOPING CHICK (WHITE LEGHORN)

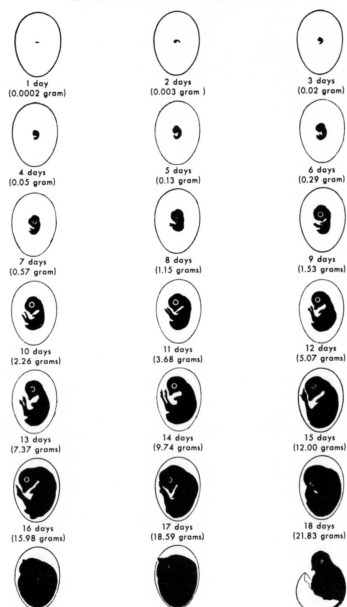

1 day
(0.0002 gram)

2 days
(0.003 gram)

3 days
(0.02 gram)

4 days
(0.05 gram)

5 days
(0.13 gram)

6 days
(0.29 gram)

7 days
(0.57 gram)

8 days
(1.15 grams)

9 days
(1.53 grams)

10 days
(2.26 grams)

11 days
(3.68 grams)

12 days
(5.07 grams)

13 days
(7.37 grams)

14 days
(9.74 grams)

15 days
(12.00 grams)

16 days
(15.98 grams)

17 days
(18.59 grams)

18 days
(21.83 grams)

19 days
(25.62 grams)

20 days
(30.21 grams)

21 DAYS
HATCHED!

FROM CORNELL BULLETIN 205, BY DR. A. ROMANOFF.

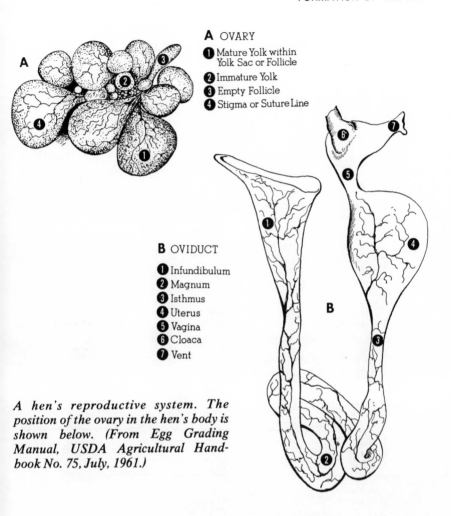

A OVARY

1. Mature Yolk within Yolk Sac or Follicle
2. Immature Yolk
3. Empty Follicle
4. Stigma or Suture Line

B OVIDUCT

1. Infundibulum
2. Magnum
3. Isthmus
4. Uterus
5. Vagina
6. Cloaca
7. Vent

A hen's reproductive system. The position of the ovary in the hen's body is shown below. (From Egg Grading Manual, USDA Agricultural Handbook No. 75, July, 1961.)

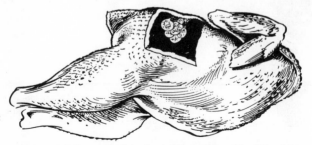

Position of the ovary in a hen. (From Egg Grading Manual, USDA Agricultural Handbook No. 75, July, 1961.)

FERTILITY OF THE EGG

Successful propagation of fowl is an exact science. There are definite steps to take to insure success. In order to have good hatchability, you must be aware of potential fertility or hatchability problems. You must know the difference in the two terms. Fertility is the percentage of eggs which are fertilized by sperm. Fertilization happens when the sperm unites with the female reproductive cell located on the yolk of the egg. The egg is fertilized in the front part of the oviduct just after the yolk is dropped into the funnel and approximately twenty-four hours before the egg is laid. Not all fertilized eggs develop into chicks. Some may die soon after fertilization, others die during various stages of incubation. Hatchability indicates the percentage of fertilized eggs that hatch into chicks.

Candling will help you to determine if you have a fertility or hatchability problem. In order to understand why you are getting poor results from a setting of eggs, you must candle them between the seventh and eighteenth days of incubation.

Eggs that appear clear with no signs of embryonic development on candling are called "clears". It could be that some of these clears had been fertilized and the resulting embryos die too early to be detected by candling. Therefore, you should break-out these eggs and examine them for evidence of embryonic development.

If fifteen to twenty percent of the clear eggs are broken out and show no signs of embryo growth, your problem is fertility. This fertility problem can be caused by a variety of factors. These will be examined carefully in order to help you solve your problem.

A candler is a wise investment to check on fertility and progress of development.

Selection of Breeding Stock

Some strains of chickens are more efficient layers than others and their eggs may hatch at a higher rate. The heritability estimate for hatchability is very low. This means the rate at which hatchability is inherited is very low. Usually environmental factors are much more important. Strains have been developed by many breeders that hatch considerably above the average for that particular breed.

The inheritance rate for fertility is practically zero, and seldom is it included in any selection program. Environmental factors are much more important. However, it has been observed that there are distinct differences between individual birds, as well as between families and strains, in producing fertile eggs. In one study it was shown that artificially inseminating thirteen million sperm from one male gave high fertility, whereas fifty million sperm are usually required for comparable fertility.

Inbreeding and crossbreeding show different results. Close inbreeding of chickens usually results in a decrease of hatchability. There is much experimental data to back this up. However, some hatching egg producers have gone overboard and have an unnecessary fear of inbreeding; to the extent that they want males of a different strain every year. Unless your flock contains less than one hundred to one hundred fifty birds inbreeding need not be a concern. The degree of inbreeding in larger flocks is usually inconsequential. Inbreeding or linebreeding are the only breeding systems that will "set" or establish a trait or characteristic.

Breeders and exhibitors mating the very rare breeds often inbreed because they have no choice as they can't get new blood. With a knowledge of genetic principles, the vitality and hatchability of inbred stock can be strengthened by crossing-in other breeds of fowl, sometimes two, three, or more varieties may be used. Risks are involved when applying these genetic principles. Hopefully, the rewards will be worth the effort, although it may well backfire because few breeders have sufficient knowledge of genetic techniques. Your state university has a poultry geneticist that can be contacted for information on this subject.

Hatchability is often increased with straincrossing. If the hatchability of a strain is low, crossing in another strain may increase hatchability. When the hatchability in the strain is high, cross breeding may result in little, if any, improvement.

When you are selecting individuals for your breeding flock you should be very careful to see that both your male and female conform to breed and varietal characteristics. There should be no serious defects such as crooked backs, beak and breast defects, knock knees, or gray eyes with irregular pupils.

Underweight individuals, as well as those showing symptoms of a diseased condition, should be removed from the flocks. If you retain yearling hens for breeding purposes, you should only use those birds which have a past record of heavy egg production.

If you have flocks or matings producing hatching eggs for broiler chickens, the breeding stock, especially the male, should be examined at broiler weight as well as at maturity. You should select for breeders, individuals showing rapid growth, feathering and good fleshing at eight weeks of age. If you select and breed from individuals that excel in these qualities, you can make great gains in improving your flock.

The most vigorous males should be selected as breeders. The less vigorous males can easily be dominated and do little to increase flock fertility. Dr. A.M. Guhl, of Kansas State University, has conducted extensive research on the social life of the chicken. His research definitely shows that some chickens dominate others. Males should be at least six months old before they are used in the breeding pen. Some of the early sexually maturing strains of Leghorns and New Hampshires may fertilize a high percentage of eggs at a younger age; while slower maturing strains and many other breeds won't reach minimum fertility until seven to eight months of age. Rapid comb development usually denotes early sexual maturity in young cockerels. However, research has shown that after the males with slower comb-growth reach sexual maturity, they have just as high fertility as their more precocious brothers.

Not all experimental data on comparative hatchability of hen and pullet eggs agree. However, it has often been shown that the highest hatchability is obtained from eggs produced by females in the latter part of their first and in their second laying years. After this time hatchability decreases. This decline in later years appears to be associated with an increase in early embryo mortality and a greater number of fullterm embryos which fail to break out of their shells. The reasons aren't clear, but it seems that the older hens lack the power of transmitting some of the vital factors to the egg. The reduced hatchability attributed to early pullet eggs may be partly due to the relatively small yolk in these eggs. Currently, in Britain and the USA, almost all hatching eggs are produced by birds in their first and only season of lay.

It is most important that your stock be free of disease. A number of diseases can be transmitted from one generation to the next through the egg. Some examples are: mycoplasmosis, lymphoid leucosis, epidemis tremors, typhoid, and pullorum. Breeding flocks should have no reactors to the rapid whole-blood test for pullorum and typhoid. All breeders should come from blood tested flocks. Bloodtesting kits and antigen are available from Stromberg's Pets Unlimited, Box 717, Fort Dodge, Iowa 50501, or Vineland Laboratories, Vineland, New Jersey 08360. To be sure and meet requirements of states which require pullorum testing, contact the veterinary science department at your state university.

Selection of Alert, Rugged, Healthy Breeders is so Important

A Husky Tom Turkey

Rugged Cornish Male

Alert White Pekin Ducks

Healthy Chinese Gander

Perky Seabright Cockerel

11

Male to Female Ratio

Females will produce eggs in the absence of a male but these eggs will not hatch — such is considered desirable for market eggs. Breeders are faced with the problem of how many males are necessary to successfully produce a high percentage of fertile hatching eggs.

Extensive studies were conducted at the Oregon Agricultural Experiment Station over a three year period. In a New Hampshire breeder flock six or seven males per hundred consistently produced high fertility. With White Leghorns it was found five males per one hundred females gave excellent results. If a larger number of males is used, it's likely to reduce fertility due to interference and fighting. This is especially true in totally confined flocks. If there's fighting between males in adjoining pens, a solid partition might be advisable. A crossmated flock of Dark Corning males and New Hampshire females needed five to six males per one hundred females to produce high fertility.

Should something happen during the hatching season to reduce the population of males below the desired number, use fewer males rather than adding additional males to those already in the flock. Adding new males may result in a fertility decline due to time and energy expended in establishing a new peck order. In many cases, three to five males will produce satisfactory fertility, but not consistently as five to seven males.

In small breeding pens or single male matings where the number of males is reduced, you should have a reserve of extra males in case a cock or cockerel is lost due to fighting, an accident or disease. Your ratio of males to females may be so low that a new male must be introduced. Therefore, if you're prepared for a possible male loss you may save your breeding program. In small breeding pens it is also wise to periodically remove the males to prevent damage to the females.

If a breeder desires to introduce new blood into his flock he should obtain the stock as hatching eggs or day old chicks. Breeder candidates should be reared on your own premises if possible. Two or three cockerel chicks should be started for each male needed in the breeding pens.

Sexual Activity

Research has shown that males increase sexual activity during the late afternoon. Sexual activity, however, isn't a reliable index of the male's reproductive capacity. Studies have shown that very sexually active birds often produced a higher percentage of dead or weak sperms than less active males. Results suggest that sex drive in fowls beyond certain limits doesn't increase fertility and might be detrimental to it. Likewise, general appearance and the body type were found not to be reliable guides to sexual activity.

It has also been found that there is preferential mating, which is a tendency for the male to mate more often with certain females. Males have favorites which often is a cause of impaired fertility in single-male breeding pens. In this case the male is responsible for the low fertility. Changing males in one study resulted in a 93% increase in fertility.

After the first year, semen volume and density decline. Studies have shown that cockerels in the fall of their first year may produce semen less dense and with fewer live spermatozoa than semen from the same bird the following spring. Semen production has been shown to increase from December thru April. Like egg production, semen production declines during the summer months. Seasonal declines in fertility are probably related to the slump in sperm production, brought on by warm weather and decreasing day length.

CHANGING MALES ...
"Multiple Cock Shift System"

It may be wise to consider changing male birds, both in small matings as well as in flock matings. Compatibility and acceptance would be of primary importance. A most interesting research bulletin of 1974 by Dr. Martin Silverudd of the Institute of Genetics, University of Lund, Sweden, explains this thoroughly. Bulletin: "Silverudd's Multiple Cock Shift System".

Proper Male Ratio

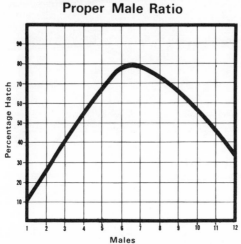

The above illustrates the proper ratio of New Hampshire males in contrast with too few males and too many males.

Rate of Lay

In naturally mated flocks, fertility is correlated with rate of lay. Females laying at a high rate of production will produce a higher percentage of fertile eggs. The larger the clutch the higher the fertility. The proportion of infertile eggs is significantly higher among females laying clutches of one to three eggs than those producing clutches of four or more eggs. Females that lay at a rapid rate remained fertile longer than those laying at a slower rate. Although it has been found that the size of the clutch is correlated to fertility, the position of the egg within the clutch has no effect on fertility, whether it is the first or last egg laid.

Length of Lay

Normally, fertility is higher during the first six months of lay and then begins a gradual decrease. This is especially true with the heavy breed, meat type chickens, where fertility may reach an unsatisfactory level after six or seven months of egg production.

Season

As previously mentioned, fertility declines during very hot weather. Cold temperatures also reduce fertility, especially when the fowl are housed in poorly insulated buildings. A male with a frozen comb is sterile until the comb heals up, which takes considerable time. Research indicates fertility among White Leghorns reaches its highest level during the spring months, sometimes showing as much as a 20% decrease in the summer. Similar studies on Barred Rocks and Rhode Island Reds showed a rapid decrease in fertility from April to July, with the lowest fertility occurring in July. As previously noted, this decrease in female fertility is correlated with a decrease in sperm production in the male.

Time of Day

There are reports that the time of day when mating takes place influences fertility. Results of different investigations suggest that for highest fertility, hens should be inseminated during the latter part of the day. There are fewer hardshelled eggs in their oviducts at that time. It would appear that it is easier for sperm in the oviduct to by-pass membrous rather than hard shelled eggs. Even under natural mating conditions fertility is higher in the afternoon.

HIGH ALTITUDE CAN   AFFECT YOUR HATCHES.

Amount of Light

Photoperiodism is the affect on the growth and development of the birds. Increasing the number of hours of light to which males are exposed was found to induce marked testicular enlargment and sperm formation during the fall and winter months when the reproduction organs were more or less inactive. Males exposed to twelve hours or more of light produced a larger amount of semen than males exposed to less light. Evidence shows that for peak response to light chickens should receive between 12 and 14 hours of light per day. The maximum response to stimulation was often reached in about one month.

Goose egg production was increased by using a fifteen hour day-length and maintaining a temperature between 60 and 68 degrees F. Sexual development of geese can be advanced by providing them with fifteen hours of light per day after they're 90 days old.

Turkeys require a minimum of fourteen hours of light to show any increase in semen production.

Dubbing

Dubbing is the removal of the comb and wattles from the males. With breeds having large combs and wattles (such as the New Hampshire and Leg-Horn) dubbing prevents frost injury to the comb and wattles, the result of this frozen comb is sterility. Males with frozen combs are inactive and sore. The males' combs freeze because of high humidity inducing rapid heat loss when

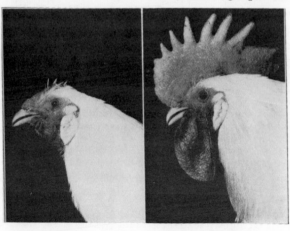

Many hatchery men and breeders find that dubbing improves fertility. Dubbing prevents frost injury. Dubbed males have no large combs to interfere with feed consumption. Male on right undubbed, male on left dubbed. Courtesy Cornell Univ. and Poultry Science.

cold. A dry cold seldom freezes the combs of healthy birds. Dubbing has many advantages. The dubbed males can eat easier from different types of feeders. The dubbed male is also not as scared or wary of other males as are undubbed males.

It is best to dub the male while he is young (eight to twelve weeks), but older males and mature males can be dubbed satisfactorily. A pair of sharp scissors or a small sharp tin snip may be used to cut off the comb and wattles. Some poultrymen use a hot iron to sear cut surfaces to reduce the bleeding. You shouldn't dub and vaccinate at the same time. Dubbing should not take place immediately before or during the hatching season. Don't dub show stock except Modern and Old English males.

Clipping Due to Heavy Plumage

Cochins, Brahmas, Orpingtons, and Wyandottes have extra heavy plumage. No doubt some other breeds could be mentioned too. These chickens require the clipping of feathers around their vents to facillitate proper mating. With the use of a heavy duty scissors or tin snips, the feathers should be clipped from an area of as much as 1½ to 2 inches on all sides of the vent. This suggests a liberal clipping. Regardless, it is a matter of necessity if you are expecting favorable hatchability of eggs from these breeds.

Clipping Crests

We recommend the clipping of crests of crested fowl primarily for sanitation reasons. This is especially important with the Polish and Houdan chickens. It is our feeling that hatchability could be somewhat affected when the males are so heavily crested that their seeing is prevented. This should only be done after you have made the close selection of your breeders.

Hormones

It has been found by injecting from a pituitary gland increases the males' production of spermatozoa. Another report shows pregnant mare's serum may be used effectively on sexually inactive male fowl. The influence of the male sex hormone on the fertility of males shows that its injections cause males to fertilize a significantly greater percentage of eggs than the noninjected. Studies concerning the thyroid gland indicate that it favorably influences spermatogenesis. The removal of the thyroid retards growth of gonads and the secondary sexual characteristics in male fowls. Thiouracil, a thyroid depressant, was found to reduce quality and the fertilizing capacity of semen. Adrenalin injections can reduce semen production and cause a degeneration of germinal tissue.

Nutrition

Nutrition, like inheritance, affects hatchability more than fertility. Proper nutrition of the breeder flock may be the most important single factor in the complex reproduction system. The breeding flock should be fed a well fortified balanced commercial breeder ration of 17-18% protein. Most commercial laying diets will not do the job. **During the hatching season, females should not be fed any supplemental grains.** The added grain may unbalance the ration by diluting the vitamins, minerals and protein content of the diet.- **Feeding of supplemental grain is a major cause of reduced hatchability.**

Restriction of total feed and/or energy, as well as certain vitamins, can reduce the fertilizing capacity of the male. One study showed some males became sterile after being fed diets deficient in Vitamin E for prolonged periods of time.

A big problem is that often they aren't getting enough feed. Males with large combs may have trouble getting food out of certain types of feeders, therefore, dubbing is very beneficial. Some males may be bullied by more aggressive ones. To help the situation you may put a few male feeders on the roosts, and/or you may cut back the upper beak of the aggressive males. Research has shown that when males lose ten to fifteen percent of the body weight, their sperm production and fertility may be affected. Losses of 25 to 30 percent may result in sterility — ZERO FERTILITY.

MANAGEMENT OF
THE BREEDER STOCK

A successful hatch depends on many factors. Great care should be taken to insure that the eggs you set in the incubator will be good eggs. You have control of the management of your stock. Poorly housed, undernourished, diseased stock will not produce quality eggs. Each individual poultryman will have his management problems to overcome. However, after careful analysis, usually the solutions to these problems will not be too difficult. Common sense and good sanitation will help you through in most cases. Success in raising chickens, waterfowl, and gamebirds depends on clean housing, satisfactory nesting areas, proper nourishment, adequate clean water and protection from disease.

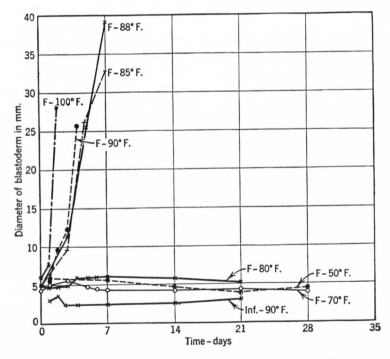

Effect of temperature on the development of the blastoderm of fertile (F) eggs. Courtesy Missouri Agr. Expt. Sta.

Housing

It is of upmost importance that the breeder flock or mating be comfortably housed. This means there should be fresh air and plenty of floor space for maximum egg production. There should be 2 to 3 and 3 to 4 square feet of floor space per hen for light and heavy breeds, respectively. Bantams, gamebirds, and other small fowl require from ½ to 1 square foot per bird.

One of the most striking areas of poor management are the very inadequate quarters that the majority of parks, zoos and memorial cemeteries provide their bands of swans. In these environments, there is limitation of space, available nesting material, feeding areas and privacy. All of which interfere with normal nesting and mating. A particular memorial park has a small pond and island for the swans, which looks very nice, but lacks adequate privacy, feeding and nesting areas. The swans have no chance to reproduce. During the winter this same park houses the swans in a small building without an adequate diet. The result is no reproduction. Many such illustrations could be related, but we feel this one example will emphasize the need for you to provide adequate pens, housing, diet and suitable environment for breeding flocks.

In bad weather you should protect your breeders from any extreme in temperature. A severe drop in temperature may cause a drop in egg production and fertility, especially when birds are located in uninsulated buildings. Extreme hot weather can also cause a drop in egg production, fertility, and hatchability

All birds, including waterfowl, should have suitable nests. Expensive or elaborate housing is not required. Since clean, uncracked eggs are desirable for hatching, the flock owner should have one properly constructed nest for each five hens. If you are using community type nests you should allow one square foot of nesting area for each five layers. Nests should always contain an adequate amount of nesting material which is replaced when soiled. Wood shavings, rice hulls, straw and excelsior are frequently used as nesting material.

Having a broody coop handy will keep the setting hens out of the nests, making more nests available for layers and helping to keep the nesting material clean. This wire bottomed coop should be suspended from the ceiling so it will sway back and forth. The swaying action, plus no feed for 24 hours, will break them up quickly.

Most nesting material is soiled by birds that use the nest for night quarters instead of roosting in the proper place. It is wise to close the nests each night. This is often done by means of a hinged nest board that acts as a step by day and a door by night so that the nests can be closed.

Artificial light may be used in the laying house to increase day length during the fall and early winter months. A light period of 13 to 14 hours (natural and artificial light) will prevent the normal fall and winter pauses in production when egg prices are higher. Lights have no harmful effect on the fertility and hatchability and they should be used during the fall and winter to obtain early chicks.

Technical advances in poultry science permits the production of high quality eggs in total confinement. Experiments have shown that the fertility and hatchability of crossmated flocks kept in confinement were no different than those of similar flocks located on range.

Over the years we have found that on rare occasions various disturbances can indirectly reduce fertility. Rats, owls, snakes, oppossums, coons, dogs, cats and other predators can upset the flock and interfere with the normal mating process. Children playing, entering pens, teasing and chasing the birds can get the flock very excited and distraught.

An automatic electric timer switch is a great convenience — can increase egg production, but does not always improve fertility-hatchibility!

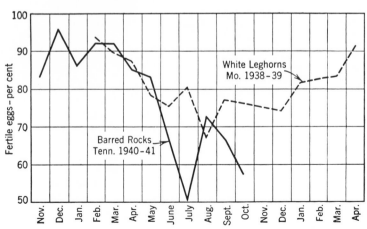

Seasonal variation in fertility of chickens. Courtesy Tennessee Agr. Expt. Sta.

Controlling Rats

The controlling of rats is a very important management practice for all fanciers, poultry farmers, and gamebird hobbyists. These vermin spread poultry diseases and parasites from farm to farm, or from the rats themselves. An adult rat will consume as much feed as a laying hen; contaminate twice as much feed as they eat; and murder baby chicks.

There are advantages and disadvantages to all methods of rat control. Be sure to follow the directions on the labels of any poisons. One method of rat control that has proved to be effective is a product called RMC Throw-Pac. It is a slow acting pelleted bait on which rats will continue to feed because they are unable to determine that it is bait which is killing them. The throw-pac may be tossed into inaccessible areas where the rats may be feeding.

Another method is to have parafeen blocks nailed to posts. This method is fair. The weather doesn't affect it and, unlike meal or poison bait boxes, they don't have to be filled on a regular basis. A disadvantage is that it must be available at all times and must be eaten five days before it will kill. There is an advantage in that birds consuming this poison will not be affected unless they eat it for a couple of days.

Water baits are prepared by mixing the poison with water and planting the bait about the farm in pans and fountains. Caution must be exercised to prevent your fowl from consuming the poison liquid. It's a lot of work as it must be kept fresh. Sometimes water baits work better than solid bait for often there's a lot of feed available for rats. Rats coming to the place for the first time, and finding water on the outside of the pens may drink it before going into the pen. Most water baits must be consumed over a period of several days before the rats will die.

Quick kill baits, if used in a limited quantity, may work well, but they do present a hazard to the poultry. Rats are quick to learn about it and may quit eating or drinking it. Poultry and pets consuming the poison will die quickly too. This isn't very safe.

It may be wise to consider professional services of exterminator companies. One method used by exterminators gives excellent results. A rodenticide resembling flour is dusted on runways or at the entrance of the burrows. The rats run through the white powder and then lick it off their feet and tail. It kills them but harms nothing else. This powder can't be bought as it's only available from exterminator companies.

Lice and Mite Control

Very little research has been conducted concerning the effect of lice and mites on fertility and hatchability. Over the years, our experience and contacts with many poultrymen, indicates infestations of lice and mites can reduce fertility and hatchability and lower egg production. We believe that the male is most often affected. Lice and mites make birds so nervous and upset that normal mating is not possible. Females are affected too, but to a lesser extent.

To point up the dramatic effect of lice on hatchability we relate this experience which pertains to a breeder flock of over 500 White Leghorn females that was a hatching egg supply flock for our hatchery several years ago. The owner had a record of good flock management, well fed stock, while maintaining very acceptable sanitation. Normally, his hatchability was in the range of 70% to 80%. All of a sudden the hatches dropped down below 50% which is a very unprofitable hatching level in a commercial hatchery. Immediately we had our flock serviceman drive out to investigate the problem. He observed that conditions appeared satisfactory, feeding up to par, and a good health level. Everything seemed satisfactory. Then he began checking individual birds and found them heavily infested with lice. Steps were taken immediately to individually delouse each bird and this was followed by a treatment of the roost. Hatchability returned to normal level within four to five weeks. We cannot over emphasize the need to keep your breeders free of lice and mites. Modern roost paints are available that treat breeders while they sleep, there is no excuse for lice and mite infestations. Write the Texas Agricultural Extension Service, College Station, Texas 77843 for a Free copy of B-1088, **External Parasites of Poultry.**

Dangers of Insecticides

While insecticides are a necessary and valuable production tool, poultrymen must be judicious in their use. Above all, follow label directions to the letter. You should be careful about giving your birds any water or foodstuffs that has been subjected to an insecticide. Some insecticides will leave a residue in both meat and eggs which may cause your birds and eggs to be condemned at the market place. Be cautious about using such sprays in areas near your poultry buildings and yards. You should know the source of any supplement grains given your flock. Always remove all feed and water before spraying or dusting in your poultry houses. PCBS (Polychloimated

Byshenyla) reduced hatchability and killed chicks to levels of only 10% in a broiler flock years ago. This amounted to a loss of millions of dollars to a national grower of broilers.

Nutrition

Commercial hens will produce well on a wide range of laying diets. This doesn't mean that the same diets are adequate for breeding flocks. Slight vitamin or mineral deficiencies may prevent an otherwise normal fertilized egg from hatching. Diet deficiencies which may reduce hatchability to zero, often will not have any ill-effect on the health or productive performance of the breeder hen.

Both males and females should be placed on a breeder diet five to six weeks before saving hatching eggs. By the end of this period the hen will have deposited all of the essential nutrients required for proper embryo development in the yolk.

Providing adequate vitamins in a breeding ration is very important. Following is a brief discussion of some vitamin and mineral deficiency symptoms. Deficiencies of various trace elements and vitamins may lead to reduced hatchability and poor chick quality. Dead embryos may exhibit conditions that reveal the particular vitamin deficiencies causing their death. A deficiency of Vitamin B-12 will cause a rapid decrease in hatchability. There's also a poorer survival rate for chickens that do hatch. Riboflavin (Vitamin B-2) deficiencies also cause poor hatchability with embryos showing clubbed down. The degree of the deficiency affects the stage at which death of the embryo takes place. An example is that a marginal deficiency of pantothenic acid may permit almost normal hatchability but poor chick viability. A greater deficiency results in heavier mortality at the end of 21 days. An extreme deficiency causes high mortality as early as twelve to sixteen days with no embryos surviving to hatch.

Biotin, choline, and manganese help prevent a condition known as perosis or slipped tendon. An acute deficiency of biotin causes high embryo mortality during the period of 72 to 96 hours of incubation. A manganese deficiency gives rise to embryos with parrot beaks and nutritional chondrodystlrophy, which is a shortening of the long bones of the embryo. A choline deficiency is unlikely as the hen seems fully able to synthesize her own requirements.

These vitamins and minerals must be included in your breeder's diet: riboflavin, pantothenic acid, Vitamin B-12, niacin, folic acid, biotin, cholin, Vitamin A, Vitamin D-3, Vitamin E, Vitamin K, manganese, phosphorus, and zinc. Most commercial breeder mashes and concentrates are sufficiently fortified and contain more than an adequate amount of these essential vitamins and minerals to insure proper embryo development.

Many breeder mash concentrates are to be fed on a 50-50 weight basis with scratch grain. You must be careful not to use too much grain. Observations have shown that when scratch grains are fed free-choice with 20% protein concentrate, the flocks will consume 65-70% scratch grain. Unless it is specified that grain be fed free-choice, try to keep the scratch consumption from going over 50%, by weight, of the ration. Breeder flocks will consume approximately 25 pounds of mash and scratch per 100 birds per day. Therefore, not more than twelve to thirteen pounds of scratch should be fed to each 100 breeders per day. The amount of feed required daily will depend on the body size, the rate of production and temperature. Mash exposed to sunlight or heat tends to lose part of its nutrition and most of its appeal. Therefore, frequent feeding of fresh feed is important.

To insure maximum feed consumption you should have 384 linear inches of hopper space for each one hundred large, standard-sized breeders. A hopper eight feet long which allows the birds to eat from both sides provides 196 linear inches of space. Two of these hoppers or five tube feeders would provide feeding space for one hundred breeders. Bantams and other small fowl require less feeder space.

Remember, most of the vitamins, minerals and protein essential for the development of the embryo and hatching of the chick are found in the mash, not in the scratch grain.

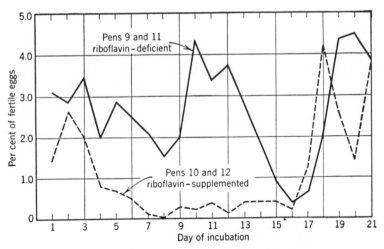

Distribution of embryonic mortality on rations containing adequate and inadequate riboflavin. (From Lepkovsky, Taylor, Jukes, and Almquist, 1938.) Courtesy California Agr. Expt. Sta.

PROPER CARE OF THE EGG BEFORE INCUBATION

Gathering

Once the egg has been laid, it must be treated with tender loving care. Hatching eggs should be gathered at least four times a day, especially if the weather is extremely hot or cold. Both extremes will reduce hatchability. Gather eggs in the late afternoon or evening to prevent them from chilling overnight.

Temperature and Humidity

Hatching eggs should be held where the temperature is 40 to 60 degrees. Reduced hatchability may result if the eggs are held at lower or higher temperatures.

Proper humidity helps control the rate at which eggs lose moisture. For best results hatching eggs should be held where the relative humidity is high, between 70-90% (but below the point where mold develops on the eggs, cases, or fillers).

Handling the Egg

Eggs intended for hatching should be handled carefully. Rough handling may addle the interior or crack the shell. Place the small end down when gathering, cartoning or casing eggs. Standing eggs on the large end may rupture many air cells. For larger eggs, such as peafowl and geese, lay them flat in a shallow box.

Containers for gathering and holding should be rigid enough to prevent eggs from crushing due to bending or twisting when under the weight of a full load of eggs. Air must be able to circulate around the eggs in order to prevent them from overheating. To avoid soilage you should use clean, preferably new, fillers and flats.

Eggs should be placed in an incubator as soon as it is convenient after being laid. They shouldn't be held any longer than seven to ten days. Unless the conditions are very good, hatchability declines after they're a week old. If they are stored under ideal situations the hatching eggs may be saved from ten days to two weeks. It should be stressed that very few flock owners have ideal egg storage facilities. Research conducted at Texas A & M University indicates that, even under ideal storage conditions, after 7 days of storage hatchability will be reduced about 1.0% per day.

If the hatching eggs are shipped a considerable distance, storage of less than seven days is very desirable. Eggs three to four weeks old are a waste of incubator space and time as the results will be most unsatisfactory.

As soon as eggs are gathered they should be placed in a 45-55 degree angle against a wall. You should alternate this tipped position at least twice a day. Write Texas Agricultural Experiment Station of Texas A & M University, College Station, Texas 77843 for a Free copy of MP-592, **Optimum Temperature and Humidity for Holding Hatching Eggs for Short Periods.**

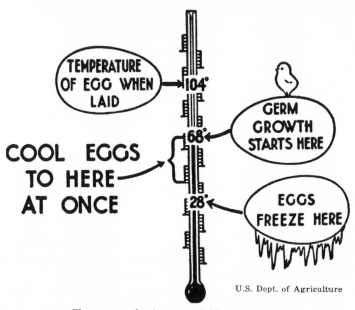

U.S. Dept. of Agriculture

Thermometer showing correct holding temperatures.

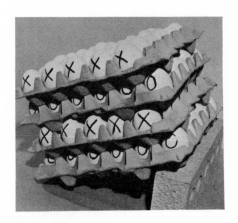

Prior to incubation while eggs are being "saved" — they should be turned or tipped at least twice a day, held in a temperature of 45 to 55 degrees.

Temperature

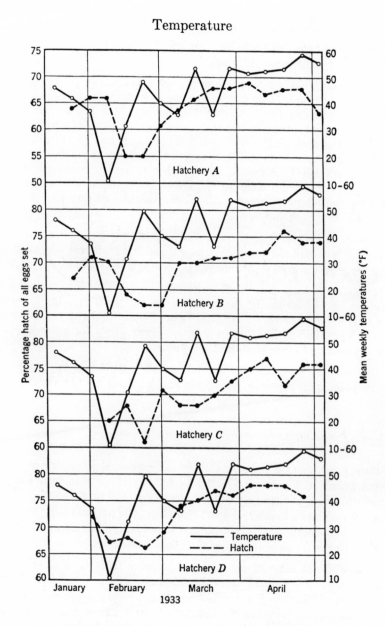

Effect of a sudden drop in temperature (weather station reports) on hatching results. Courtesy Missouri Agr. Expt. Sta.

Due to the labor required to clean soiled eggs and the possible reducing of hatchability due to most cleaning methods, every effort should be made to produce a high percentage of clean eggs. With proper management, only a small number of eggs will require cleaning. To clean the egg properly you should buff eggs with coarse sandpaper.

If contamination is extensive and the egg is needed for hatching due to its intrinsic value, there's no alternative but to wash it. If the eggs must be washed the water should be warmer than the eggs (115-120°F) and should contain a germical compound at the recommended level. The higher temperature of the wash fluid expands the contents of the egg preventing the solution or bacteria from being drawn into the egg through the pores. Washing won't affect embryonic development as the egg is exposed to the high temperature for only a short time. Follow the manufacturer's directions concerning the temperature of wash water, duration of dip, and the concentration. The egg should be dried before storage.

Ideally, neither floor eggs nor soiled eggs should be incubated. These eggs are liable to explode, contaminating the incubator and causing naval infection. Eggs may also be disinfected by fumigation.

It's also important that the hatching eggs do not come into contact with grease or oil as petroleum products tend to seal the shell, preventing a transfer of oxygen to the embryo. Write the Texas Agricultural Extension Service of Texas A&M University, College Station, Texas 77843 for a free copy of MP-576, **Cleaning Eggs—Method, Cost, Value.**

Some hatcherymen and authorities feel all eggs should be fumigated. This viewpoint is expressed in our chapter entitled Sanitation Procedures.

Effect of Altitude

If the hatching eggs are to be shipped, air express is a practical means of transportation. In a study conducted by Jull, hatching eggs were shipped from Washington, D.C. to Los Angeles and return, and to Miami and return. The maximum altitude reached was 12,000 feet. The hatchability wasn't impaired by these shipments. It is important to note these shipments were large quantity shipments, not small shipments thrown into mail bags.

In a study of reduced atmospheric pressure the effects of simulated altitudes from 6,500 to 90,000 feet on hatchability were measured. There was no significant reduction in hatchability until the pressure was reduced to .5 inches of mercury (equivalent of an altitude of 90,000 feet). Eggs held at this pressure for twelve hours daily for three days gave hatchability of only 45% compared to 92% for eggs held at an altitude of 200 feet. This decrease in hatchability was associated with an excess loss of water from the eggs.

Another study reported that by increasing the atmospheric pressure during incubation to 1½ times normal, death of embryos will result. Most died between the sixth and tenth days, about 14% survived to the seventeenth day of incubation. There is a need for additional experiments to establish the effect hatchability of **increased** atmospheric pressure during the holding period.

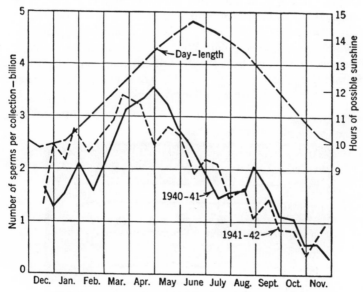

Relation to season of sperm production of Rhode Island Red cockerels. Like egg production, sperm production appears to be influenced by length of day. Courtesy Tennessee Agr. Expt. Sta.

Packing Eggs for Shipment

Too many breeders who ship eggs are not aware of the importance of proper packing in order to secure maximum hatchability. At best, shipped hatching eggs present some disadvantages as compared to eggs that are not shipped. This statement primarily applies to small lot shipments. Eggs shipped in large 30 dozen egg cases, typically via Air Freight, usually are not harmed greatly by shipping.

Small lot shipments are typically sold by the setting of 15 eggs. Just why that number, rather than by the dozen...we are not sure when, where or how this all started. Logically, most of the larger standard breed hens can easily "cover" more than a dozen eggs. Thus, we will discuss packing hatching eggs for shipments in lots of 15, 30, 45 and 60 eggs. Some 50 to 100 years ago eggs were sold by 50's and 100's as well as settings.

Most shippers have ready access to the dozen size egg cartons in which eggs are packed for sale at retail stores. These provide an excellent "inner container". FIRST, make sure that you are shipping eggs that will hatch, when properly incubated. We recommend that you ship eggs just as soon after laying as possible, as the length of time spent in transit plays a very important part in the final outcome. Never ship eggs that are more than seven days old. Prior to shipment make sure eggs have been held at a temperature of 45-60 degrees F. and relative humidity of 75%. SECONDLY, ship only clean eggs. The simple use of an egg buffer or sandpaper is most adequate. Do not wash eggs before shipping. Washing removes the protective coating and allows bacteria to penetrate the shell. If anything causes an unfavorable reaction to buying hatching eggs, it is the arrival of dirty, filthy eggs. Dirty eggs can also transmit disease from flock to flock.

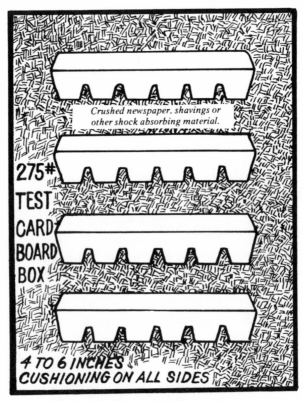

The above illustrates recommended packaging to reasonably assure a safe, sound arrival.

Two of these dozen size cartons will be needed for the 15 two ounce (large) eggs. It will require three cartons to ship 15 larger size eggs as it is best to use alternate spaces to avoid shell to shell contact. Not all, but most breeders will include an extra egg or so. Some considerate breeders, when they know the hatchability of their eggs has dropped some, may include five or six extra eggs, which helps create good feelings and good will. To protect the eggs from both jarring and bouncing about in the carton, provide some type of cushioning. Well known APA poultry Judge John Wunderlich recommends lightly moistened fine wood shavings or saw dust as packing. This helps the eggs maintain their moisture content and prevents dehydration during transit. No doubt there is other packing material which can be moistened in this manner. DO NOT SOAK THE SHAVINGS so that they are dripping wet, just reasonably moistened.

If possible place all shipping materials (cartons, packing material, wrapping paper, etc.) in the egg storage area so they will be damp and cool. This will help to reduce sweating during shipment. No doubt lightly moistened tissue or newspaper could be used, wrapping each individual egg. Egg cartons should be sealed as tight as possible. This can be done with scotch, masking or freezer tape. These steps are necessary to assure the safe, satisfactory arrival of the hatching eggs.

It is very important to use an outer shipping container that can take some abuse. Years ago two containers were often used, wooden and woven bushel baskets. Now, such are not often readily available and would be too expensive. So, presently the popular container is the cardboard box. As a shipper of hatching eggs you must be aware of the vast difference in cardboard boxes. Some cardboard boxes are of such heavy, durable stock they have the strength of light wooden boxes. We would recommend shipping in cardboard boxes showing a "bursting test" rating of 275 pounds per square inch. A 275 pound test box 9x12x12 will support the weight of a 200 pound man easily. Bursting test information is indicated on most cardboard boxes. Such heavy-duty cardboard boxes are available from liquor stores and shops dealing in fine china and glassware.

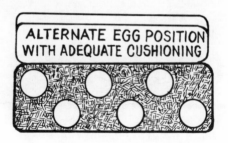

ALTERNATE EGG POSITION WITH ADEQUATE CUSHIONING

Select a box that is large enough to provide adequate protection for the eggs. It is much wiser to use a box which is too large, with adequate cushioning, than one which is too small. Keep in mind the box may have to protect those eggs from SOME VERY EXCESSIVE ABUSES. Your box of eggs may have the misfortune of being at the bottom of the stack, or it may be under a heavy pile of mail bags. Although there are postal regulations providing that boxes of hatching eggs can NOT BE THROWN IN MAIL BAGS, the fact is, a vast majority of hatching eggs, regardless of the prominently displayed fragile labels warning for careful handling, ARE TOSSED IN THE MAIL BAGS for faster handling.

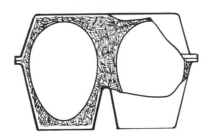

Eggs should be individually wrapped in tissue, newspaper, or oat hulls to prevent jarring within egg carton. Slightly moistened, fresh clean shavings are ideal too. This protects eggs as well as helps hold both temperature and moisture.

After selection of a box which is both large and strong enough, you may proceed to place the egg cartons in the larger box. Liberal use of crushed newspapers should be placed on all sides of the egg cartons. Strive to provide about an inch of crushed newspapers between each of the egg cartons, preferably more. All the time, while packing these eggs for shipment, bear in mind. . ."THIS BOX MAY DROP TEN FEET off a mail truck while unloading." Or. . .THIS BOX MAY BE TOSSED TEN FEET INTO A MAIL BAG." Or. . .another unhappy thought. . ."THIS BOX MAY BE AT THE BOTTOM OF A PILE OF MAIL BAGS WEIGHING ONE THOUSAND POUNDS!"

Mr. W.G. Stach excells in shipping bantam eggs in boxes designed for shipping glassware to gift shops — ONE EGG per compartment.

Mr. John Wabeck, noted White Rock Breeder, also emphasizes the need for a strong outer cardboard box to insure safe delivery of eggs. Start by lining the bottom of the box with four inches of crumpled paper. Wrap each egg individually in a double layer of newspaper, tucking in the sides as you proceed. Place the wrapped eggs side by side in the mail box making sure that there is crumpled paper around the sides of the box to act as a cushion. Place the eggs in the box small end down. When the first layer of eggs is finished, place a thick layer of crumpled newspaper over it and start your second layer. Make sure you have about four inches of crumpled paper at the top of the box over the last layer. In this way each egg will be protected on all sides and the container will be cushioned on all sides as well.

A few breeders have found it wise to use 25 size chick boxes to ship 15 eggs. Somehow the postal employees respect it as though it were a box of baby chicks.

The final stage of preparation is to securely tie or tape the box tightly shut. DO IT WELL. Give it the appearance of thoughtful care and diligence. Address the box very clearly using the shipping labels suggested by Stromberg's to insure safe delivery of the eggs. Use a black felt pen to show to whom you are shipping the eggs, as well as your name and address, as the shipper. A typed shipping label will be more business like and adds dignity to your shipment. By all means, show the postal zip number and the phone number of your customer, as this could speed up delivery. It is recommended you ship on Mondays to prevent weekend lay overs, for the rapid delivery of the eggs is extremely important.

Most breeders ship with postage charges extra. There are some definite advantages in that COD shipments have some insurance protection. Your package may receive extra consideration if you will write on the box: "OUT-SIDE MAIL, Postal Regulations Service Manual 334-525 and 334-53." Unfortunately, many postal employees are not aware of these regulations and will not bother to look them up. . .and as the saying goes "COULD CARE LESS." Remember to use a large, strong box with the four to six inches of cushioning. When using COD shipping, you will receive your postage money paid out, usually in about a week through postal channels.

The United Parcel Service has been known to handle hatching egg shipments. When they do accept eggs. . .it is with an understanding of NO GUARANTEE. UPS is most efficient, handles most all packages with machinery, belt conveyors, and takes approximately half the delivery time of the U.S. Postal Service.

Greyhound package express and most of the truck lines that deal in local shipments will accept hatching eggs if they serve the destination of your shipment.

OUTSIDE MAIL!

POSTAL REGULATION SERVICE MANUAL 334.525 AND 334.53

Fragile . . .

HATCHING
EGGS

HANDLE WITH CARE

Special label for shipping hatching eggs — intended to keep eggs out of the mail bags per Postal Regulations.

SELECTION OF THE HATCHING EGGS

There are certain characteristics which are related to hatchability.

Size and Weight of the Egg

The size or weight of the egg is related to hatchability. Usually the average sized eggs hatch better than eggs which are larger or smaller than the flock's average. Many studies have shown that in a given flock of chickens the largest eggs have the poorest hatchability. Egg size has a fairly high heritability. Rejection of small eggs will help maintain good egg size in the progeny. In bantams you may help to reduce adult size by consistently selecting for small egg size.

Set only average weight eggs weighing 2 to 2½ ounces per egg for most light breeds. This means that eggs weighing between 24 and 27 ounces per dozen are preferred. Even though average size eggs hatch the best, eggs from some individuals and some flocks weighing up to 30 ounces per dozen hatched satisfactorily. Chicks hatched from small eggs are smaller than chicks hatched from larger eggs. NOTE: There is no correlation between hatch weight and 8 week body weight.

Shell Thickness

Eggs with thick, strong shells hatch better than eggs with weak thin shells. The egg shell thickness can be measured by floating eggs in a salt solution of various concentrations. The specific gravity of an egg is highly correlated with the thickness of the shell.

The perosity of the shell determines the rate of moisture loss during storage and incubation. It is a highly inherited characteristic, so continue to use eggs with good shell texture. Very thin shelled eggs and eggs with rough or abnormal shells can be detected by appearance. Checks or cracked eggs can be detected by candling or belling (lightly tapping eggs together) with abnormal sounding eggs being rejected. Uncracked, good quality eggs will have a clear ring.

Some people believe that eggs with shells that appear mottled before the candler have poor hatchability. Results of studies have shown these hatch as well as others.

Shape of the Egg

A person should avoid setting odd shaped eggs. Egg shape is largely an inherited characteristic and is extremely important in the production of market eggs where shape helps determine the consumer grade. If you want stock to lay quality eggs, then the importance of closely selected eggs is of great significance.

With rare show stock, a breeder will feel inclined to set all eggs, as very often he has only a few eggs. Each of his eggs are more important than the eggs from the higher volume egg laying stock.

Odd, irregular shaped eggs should not be set.

Yolk Characteristics

Certain studies have shown that the ratio of the yolk to white has an effect on the hatchability. Eggs with an average ratio of two parts white to one part yolk had a higher hatchability than eggs having larger or smaller ratios of these two components.

A study found that the arbitrary grades of yolk color had a descending hatching power. The lightest color yolk had the poorest hatchability. This could be due to the fact that the birds laying the lightest egg yolks may not have received adequate Vitamin A. Light colored yolks may also indicate a long period of lay that depletes stores of body reserve.

The results of several studies comparing albumen score and hatching power are conflicting and inconclusive.

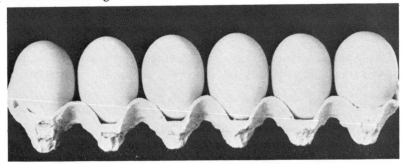

Only uniform shaped eggs should be set.

Causes of Abnormalities

Internal layers are a very common form of abnormal egg formation. The yolk falls from the ovary, but for some reason the funnel portion of the oviduct fails to pick-up or catch the ova (yolk). It is not clear why the oviduct fails to function properly. The problem may be related to a disease condition or it may be due to some abnormal physical structure. As the yolk accumulates in the hen's body cavity, her walk begins to resemble that of a penguin. Peritonitis or infections of the body cavity lining may accompany this accumulation of yolks.

There may be premature expulsion of eggs. These soft shelled eggs may be the result of age or a calcium shortage.

Eggs held in the oviduct for an extended period may cause misshaped shells especially if a second egg reaches the uterus before the first egg is laid.

About 65% of double yolked eggs result from the simultaneous development of two yolks which drop in the oviduct at the same time. Twenty-five percent are caused by simultaneous ovulation of two ova which have developed in a normal sequence, one of which prematurely ovulated. The remaining ten percent is caused from successive development and simultaneous release of two ova, one whose release was delayed for a day.

Yolkless eggs are usually dwarf size and not common. These usually contain bits of yolk material or some foreign body which is believed to be instrumental in initiating the secretion of albumen and the formation of the envelope.

Dirty, odd, freak shaped eggs should not be set.

A misshaped egg may be caused by abnormalities of the oviduct, which may be the result of disease or injury. The flattening and wrinkling of the egg shell has been found to be due to constrictions in the walls of the isthmus and uterus and by the presence of two separate eggs in the uterus.

Poor shells and odd shapes can result from improper vaccination or from vaccination that occurs too late in life or during production.

Studies have shown that most so-called meat spots are blood spots which have degenerated. Some clots are due to hemorrhages that occur before ovulation. Research has also shown the tendency to produce blood spots is inherited.

Although they are rare, more consumers than you would think complain about finding a worm in an egg. The digestive, urinary and reproductive systems have a common junction just inside the hen's body — the cloaca. Normally, worms move down the digestive system to the cloaca and then to the outside through the vent. Rather than passing out the vent a worm will move up the oviduct where it is encased in a developing egg.

An egg within an egg is extremely rare but does happen in nature. A perfectly developed egg for some unknown reason will move back up the oviduct where it meets a yolk traveling down the oviduct. Both yolk and shell will move down the oviduct together where both are encased in albumen, shell membranes, and shell.

REASONS FOR POOR HATCHES

1. Infertile eggs.
2. Eggs too old when set.
3. Parent stock weak, unhealthy, or fed a nutritionally deficient diet.
4. Improper care of eggs prior to incubation.
5. Shell contamination.
6. Eggs not turned often enough.
7. Temperatures too high, too low, or too variable during incubation.
8. Too little humidity in the incubator or occasionally too much.
9. Improper ventilation.
10. Oxygen starvation.

---

10 Commandments For Successful Hatching

1. Set only fresh eggs, less than 7 days old.
2. Follow precisely factory incubator instructions.
3. Feed especially well 6 weeks prior to saving eggs.
4. Make certain of no lice or mite problem.
5. Maintain the best of sanitation.
6. Provide adequate feeder and fountain space.
7. Prior to incubation keep eggs at 45 to 55 degrees.
8. Prior to incubation — turn or "tip" eggs twice per day.
9. Observe to make sure of active male birds.
10. Watch carefully to maintain healthy breeders.

INCUBATING THE EGG

Preparing for Incubation

Eggs which have been in transit should be stored in a cool place (45-60°- F) 24 hours prior to incubation. Remove eggs from the cooler for a period of three to six hours before placing the eggs in the incubator to remove the chill. Cold eggs placed next to warmed eggs may tend to retard the embryo growth of those eggs already in the incubator.

There are certain physical requisites for successful incubation. In natural incubation the hen instinctively takes care of these factors. A close, persistent sitter may have to be removed from the nest once a day to allow proper ventilation of the eggs. The natural movements of the hen will insure that the eggs are reasonably evenly heated and turned often enough to prevent embryos from adhering to the membranes. It may surprise you to learn that a hen will turn (shift) her eggs an average of 96 times in 24 hours, according to work conducted by Marlowe Olsen in the 1920's as a part of his thesis at the Iowa State University. Incubators used by most commercial hatcheries automatically turn (change the position) the eggs once each hour. This is also true with the Marsh Automatic Roll-X Incubator.

The "golden rule" of artificial incubation is: Read and carry out the manufacturer's instructions. FOLLOW DIRECTIONS! We will provide you some general guidelines, but remember that the manufacturer's instructions are very important and should be followed to the letter.

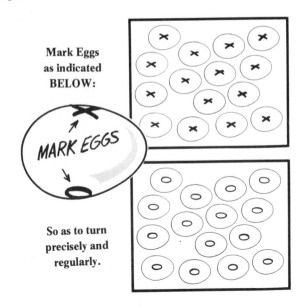

Mark Eggs as indicated BELOW:

MARK EGGS

So as to turn precisely and regularly.

Positioning and Turning the Egg

By the end of the fourth day of incubation the embryo has come to lie on top of the yolk on its left side. The head and tail now lie close together in a 'C' shape with its back toward the air cell. (See diagram) Late on the third day the allantois (embryonic lungs) grows out from the umbillicus (later called naval), through which the yolk sac and its contents are drawn on the 20th day of incubation, proceeds up over the right side of the embryo and goes to the air cell, located above the chick's back, where it adheres to the inner shell membrane. When the 12th day arrives, almost the entire shell is lined with this allantois or network of fine blood vessels through which the embryo breathes. Formation and adhesion of the extra embryonic membranes, coupled with blood vessel location, limits the embryo's movement, but the whole body twists and turns continuously.

Around the 12th or 14th day, the embryo is forced to assume a lengthwise position within the egg. In making this change, the head always seeks the highest point in the egg. Should the small end of the egg be up at this time the embryo will assume a position with its head in the small end away from the air cell. The embryo can continue to move from one end of the egg to the other until its size prevents such a shift. At this point its position is fixed.

The proper position of the chick when ready to hatch is with its head in the air cell end of the egg. Therefore, when the egg is in a vertical position the large air cell end should be up. If the embryo is positioned with its head in the small end of the egg, it's practically impossible for the chick to hatch, although it may pip the shell.

Nature intended the air cell to be located in the large end of the egg and the large end to be elevated. The chick's head goes to the highest point in the egg because of gravity and instinct. At hatching time, the chick receives its first breath of life when its beak punctures the egg shell. Therefore, a different position is contrary to Nature's laws and will result in poor hatchability. When an egg is laying on its side the natural shape sufficiently elevates the large end.

THE IMPORTANCE of frequent turning is stressed with the Automatic Marsh Incubator with eggs turned "shifted" once — EACH HOUR!

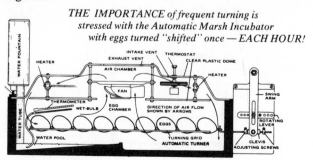

Turning Eggs

Turning reduces the tendencies of the embryo to stick to the shell membranes. Developing embryos will readily adhere to the surrounding membranes if the eggs remain in the same position too long. Not only does frequent turning increase hatchability, but it also reduces early embryonic mortality and certain embryo malpositions (chick in wrong position at hatching time).

It is critical that all hatching eggs be turned at least three (3) times per day for the first ten days of incubation. More frequent turning usually increases hatchability. As previously discussed, some incubators are equipped with automatic turning devices which can be regulated to rotate the eggs at different intervals. Normally eggs are turned every hour through the first 18 days of incubation. However, in small incubators where hand turning is required, it is not practical to turn the eggs every hour. These eggs should be turned a minimum of three and preferably five times per day. It is important that eggs be turned an odd number of times so that the overnight position will be staggered from day to day. We recommend that you maintain a definite schedule for turning your eggs. An excellent method for insuring that the eggs are turned uniformly is to put an 'X' on one side and an 'O' on the opposite side. Then you can always tell when the eggs have been turned because either all O's or all X's are visible at the same time. Keep a record of all turning activities to insure eggs are turned regularly. This record will provide an excellent reference for trouble shooting poor hatches.

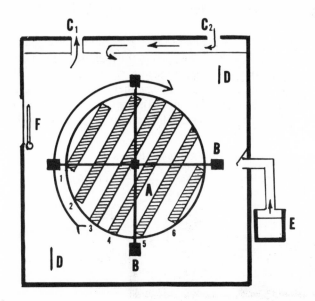

Egg turning arrangement in the large Humidaire Petersime and Robbins Incubators

When turning eggs in still-air incubators, move them to a different part of the setting tray to offset temperature variation which occur within incubators having no fans.

Regardless of the turning method, it is very important to avoid shocks and jarring the first 24 hours of incubation in order to prevent damage to the vitalline blood vessels which develop from the blood island. Interruption of the vitalline blood system formation may result in a high rate of mortality among the young embryos, and reduce the hatchability of the remaining embryos.

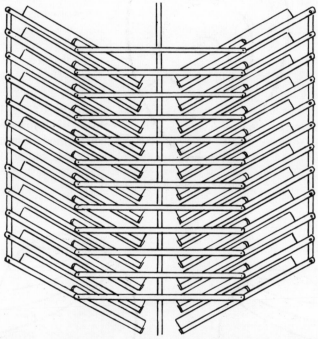

Egg turning arrangement in the large Chickmasters. Also, Buckeye and Smith Incubators of years ago.

CAUTION: ALWAYS Follow Directions of Incubator Manufacturer.

Observing the Incubation Progress

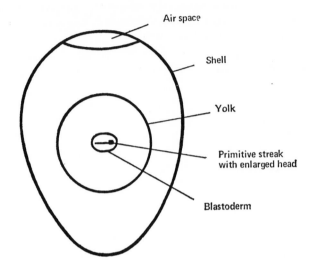

Correct position of 18-hr embryo

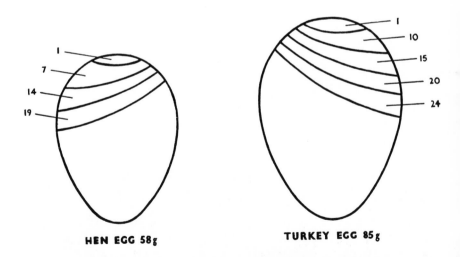

HEN EGG 58 g   **TURKEY EGG 85 g**

Correct size of air space at different stages of incubation (Nos. indicate days)

Temperature

All living creatures have an optimum temperature range in which they flourish. When their environmental temperature falls below or exceeds this range, there is a disruption of normal body functions as the plant or animal tries to adjust to its surroundings. If an adjustment is impossible, life stops. So it is with the developing embryo within the egg. Temperature is the most critical factor in determining success or failure of a hatchery operation.

Actually, the germ begins to develop before the fertilized egg leaves the warm confines (107°F) of the hen's body. About 3 hours after fertilization the newly formed single cell divides and makes two cells. Cell division continues so that by the time the egg is laid there are many cells grouped in a small whitish spot visible on the upper surface of the egg yolk.

When the egg is laid and its temperature drops below 80°F, cell division ceases. Cooling eggs at a temperature of 45-60°F will not kill the embryo, and it will be dormant until placed in an incubator to resume its development. Holding eggs at temperatures above 80°F prior to incubation will cause a slow growth which leads to weakening and eventual death of the embryo. If eggs are subjected to temperatures below 40°F prior to incubation the embryo will die.

Particular care should be taken to operate the incubator at the exact temperature recommended by the manufacturer for that particular make and model.

Should you read instructions for operating several different makes of incubators you may think that eggs will hatch at many different temperatures. This is not true. The amount of heat reaching the embryos must be the same in all machines. Differences in thermostat, egg and thermometer location, as well as differences in the ventilation systems, and distribution of heat make it necessary to operate different makes of incubators at varying temperatures in order to provide the same temperature at the embryo level.

Basically there are two types of incubators — forced draft and still-air or natural draft machines. Forced draft incubators use a continuously operating fan to evenly distribute the warm air to all areas of the incubator. This makes it possible to have several layers of hatching eggs incubating at the same time. While still-air or natural-draft incubators have no mechanical means of moving air within the machine and must depend on the upward movement of heated air for ventilation and heat dissipation. There are some very large differences in the temperature of the various layers of air in a still-air machine. For this reason there is only one level within each still-air incubator at which eggs can successfully be incubated. This means that only one layer of eggs can be successfully incubated in these types of machines, which place them at a great disadvantage in a large commercial operation.

NO FAN – RADIATION
"Conventional" INCUBATORS

FOWL	DAYS	SCHOOL OBSERVATION	BROWER NO. 846		UN-LISTED INCUBATOR
Chickens - Bantams	21	100°-101°	84°-85°	102°-103°	89°-90°	...
Ducks	28	101°-102°	87°-88°	102°-103°	87°-88°	...
Geese	29-31	101°-102°	90°-92°	101-1/2°-102-1/2°	90°-92°	...
Guineas	28	...	...	102°-103°	89°-90°	...
Pea Fowl	28	...	...	...	...	...
Pheasants	23-26	101°-102°	85°-87°	101-1/2°-102-1/2°	85°-87°	...
Golden Pheasants	23-24	...	...	...	...	...
Ringneck Pheasants	24-1/2	...	...	...	...	...
Quail	23-24	101°	90°	101-3/4°-102°	90°-91°	...
Turkey	28	100°-102°	85°-87°	100°-102°	85°-87°	...
Partridge	22-23	...	...	...	...	...
Crested Greenwood Partridge	22-23	...	...	...	...	...
Barthroated Tree Partridge	22-23	...	...	...	...	...
Mute Swan	37	...	...	...	...	...
Nene Geese	29	...	...	...	...	...
Ruffed Grouse	23	...	...	...	...	...
Rhea	35-40	...	...	...	...	...
Ostrich	40-42	...	...	...	...	98°
Eastern Crowned Crane	30	...	...	...	...	85°
Razor Billed Curassow	...	...	...	...	...	...
Emu	58-61	...	...	...	...	...

FAN – FORCED AIR INCUBATORS

FOWL	DAYS	HUMIDAIRE		PETERSIME		LEAHY	
Chickens - Bantams	21	99-1/2°	85°-86°	99-3/4°	82°-84°	99-3/4°	85°-87°
Ducks	28	99-1/2°	85°-90°	99-1/2°	84°-85°	99-1/2°	84°-86°
Geese	29-31	99-1/2°	86°-92°	99-1/2°	84°-86°	99-1/4°	86°-88°
Guineas	28	99-1/2°	82°-85°	99-1/2°	82°-84°	99-3/4°	83°-85°
Pea Fowl	28	...	...	99-1/4°	83°-85°	99-1/4°	83°-85°
Pheasants	23-26	...	...	99-3/4°	82°-84°	99-3/4°	82°-84°
Golden Pheasants	23-24	99-1/2°	82°-85°	...	...	...	...
Ringneck Pheasants	24-1/2	99-1/2°	82°-85°	...	...	99-3/4°	84°-86°
Quail	23-24	99-1/2°	82°-85°	99-3/4°	84°-86°	99-3/4°	84°-86°
Turkey	28	99-1/2°	81°-83°	99-1/4°	83°-85°	99-1/4°	83°-85°
Partridge	22-23	99-1/2°	82°-85°	99-1/4°	...	99-3/4°	80°-82°
Crested Greenwood Partridge	22-23	99-1/2°	82°-85°	99-1/2°	86°-87°	99-3/4°	...
Barthroated Tree Partridge	22-23	...	...	99-3/4°	86°-87°	...	...
Mute Swan	37	99-1/2°-99-3/4°	79°	...	...	...	...
Nene Geese	29	99-1/2°	79°	...	...	...	...
Ruffed Grouse	23	...	...	...	...	...	...
Rhea	35-40	97°	75°	97-1/2°	82°	...	...
Ostrich	40-42	...	86°	...	...	...	...
Eastern Crowned Crane	30	99-1/2°-99-3/4°	86°	...	...	...	...
Razor Billed Curassow	...	99-1/2°-99-3/4°	85°	...	...	...	...
Emu	58-61	96°	75°	97.5°	80°	...	...

A HEN "TURNS" HER EGGS FREQUENTLY!

According to a research study at the Iowa State University in 1930 by M. W. Olsen, a sitting hen will "turn" (shift) her eggs an average of 96 times in 24 hours. Most large commercial incubators, including the Marsh Roll-X Automatic, turn eggs once each hour to achieve efficient hatches.

Holding Eggs Too Long

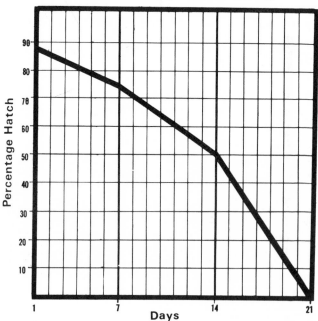

PET FOWL MAY DISAPPOINT YOU!

Your special favors toward a favorite bird may disrupt their natural inclination to mate. No research confirms this, however, some breeders have found this to be true. Your extra kindness toward a pet could result in their not accepting a mate.

MISCELLANEOUS BIRDS — Name of Incubator Not Specified			
FOWL	**DAYS**	**TEMPERATURE**	**HUMIDITY**
Canary	14	99-3/4°	82°-84°
Finch.	14	99-3/4°	82°-84°
Parakeet	14-15	99-3/4°	82°-84°
Pigeon	18-19	99-3/4°	82°-84°
Parrot	28	99-3/4°	82°-84°
Cockatiel.	21	99-1/2°	85°
Vulture	28-39	99-1/2°	85°
Eagle.	42-49	99-1/2°	85°
Currasow	28-32	99-1/2°	85°

While the above can be incubated in Incubators, some can present a problem as to feeding them — getting them to take nourishment to sustain them.

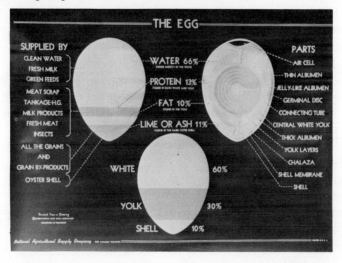

MARSH AUTOMATIC ROLL-X OPERATING RECOMMENDATIONS				
FOWL	**DAYS**	**TEMPERATURE RANGE**	**HYGROMETER TEMPERATURE**	**ROOM TEMPERATURE**
Chicken	21	98-1/2°-100°	84°-86°	76°
Ducks (Except Muscovy)	28	98-1/2°-99°	82°-85°	75°
Muscovey Ducks	35-37	98-1/2°-99°	82°-85°	75°
Goose.	30-34	98-1/2°-99°	82°-85°	75°
Turkey	28	99°-99-1/2°	80°-82°	80°
Quail.	23	99°-99-1/2°	82°-85°	80°
Pheasant	22-24	99°-99-1/2°	80°-83°	80°

In most forced-draft incubators the temperature will range from 99 to 100°F where the setting and hatching compartments are combined (single stage). Where separate hatchers (multi-stage) are used the temperature can be considerably reduced the last three days of incubation. Temperatures recommended usually range from 96° to 98°F, again it should be stressed to closely follow the manufacturer's directions.

In still-air or natural-draft incubators the bottom of both the thermometer and thermostat should be located on a level with the top of the eggs. The temperature should range from 100 to 103°F but should not exceed 103° for more than a few minutes. Adjust the thermostat so that the heat will come on at 100° and shut off at 103°.

Some incubator thermometers are misleading, they may indicate 103°F as the ideal temperature and 100°F as being too low. This may be correct for a particular incubator, but would not hold true for other machines. Remember to follow the manufacturer's recommendations, not the thermometer's direction for more than likely it was designed for a specific make of incubator.

The actual incubator temperature should be checked just as soon as possible after the pilot light indicates the thermostat has shut the heat off. This should be the highest temperature to which the eggs are exposed. You will be unable to determine the highest temperature within the incubator, if you read the thermometer while the heat is on; as the temperature will continue to climb and any measurement or reading will be lower than the actual maximum temperature.

During the last three days of incubation, the temperature should be watched for five minutes after the heat goes off in order to determine if the heat generated by the eggs themselves is pushing the temperature up above the critical mark.

Likewise, the low temperature should be measured at the instant the pilot light indicator shows the heat has been turned on.

Most research indicates that the best hatches result at a continuous embryo temperature of 99.5°F.

Normal embryo development and time of hatch depends on the proper environmental temperatures. When temperatures are above optimum level, hatches will be early and hatchability will be reduced. Embryonic mortality will be especially high during the last week of incubation (19th day for chickens and 25th for turkeys). Chicks that hatch will be smaller and less alert due to an abnormal loss of water or dehydration. Unless these chicks are given special attention they will not start to drink or eat. Their muscles lose resilience and the chicks dry up and soon die.

Leahy Incubator Chart of Condensed Operating Instructions.

Requirements	Chicken Bantam	Turkey Peacock	Duck	Mus-covey Duck	Goose	Bob-White Quail	Co-turnix Quail	Chukar Part-ridge	Phea-sant	Guinea
1—Incubation period	21 days	28 days	28 days	35 days	30 days	23-24 days	17 days	23-24 days	23-26 days	28 days
2—Operating Temperature	99¾ degrees	99¾ degrees	99½ degrees	99½ degrees	99¾ degrees	99¾ degrees	99¾ degrees	99¾ degrees	99¾ degrees	99¾ degrees
3—Wet-bulb reading, when all eggs set at one time or separate hatcher is used	85-87 degrees	83-85 degrees	84-86 degrees	84-86 degrees	86-88 degrees	84-86 degrees	84-86 degrees	80-82 degrees	82-84 degrees	83-85 degrees
4—Wet-bulb reading for continuous or intermittent setting and hatching in the same incubator	84-86 degrees	83-86 degrees	•	•	•	•	•	•	•	•
5—Wet-bulb reading after completion of turning period	90-94 degrees	90-94 degrees	90-94 degrees	90-94 degrees	90-94 degrees	90-94 degrees	90-94 degrees	90-94 degrees	90-94 degrees	90-94 degrees
6—Open ventilation holes one-fourth	10th day	14th day	12th day	15th day	at once	12th day	8th day	12th day	12th day	14th day
7—Open ventilation holes further if incubator is full	18th day	25th day	25th day	30th day	25th day	20th day	14th day	20th day	20th day	24th day
8—Use cross wires in trays	USE THE NECESSARY EGG POSITIONERS									
9—Use of "U" turning wire in tray with proper egg positioner	YES	YES	YES	YES	Use Goose Egg Turning Wire	YES	YES	YES	YES	YES
10—Do not turn eggs after day	19th day	25th day	25th day	31st day	25th day	21st day	15th day	21st day	20-23rd day	25th day

*Check Special Instructions for continuous setting and hatching in same incubator. When all eggs are set at one time or you use a separate hatcher, reduce operating temperature one or two degrees when eggs start to pip.

Incubation Period and Incubator Operation for Eggs of Domestic Birds.

Requirements	Chicken and Bantam	Turkey	Duck	Muscovy Duck	Goose	Guinea	Pheasant	Peafowl	Bobwhite Quail	Coturnix Quail	Chukar Partridge	Grouse	Pigeon
Incubation Period (days)	21	28	28	35-37	28-34	28	23-28	28-30	23-24	17	23-24	25	**17**
Forced-Air Operating Temperature[2] (degrees F., dry bulb)	99¾	99¼	99½	99½	99¼	99¾	99¾	99¼	99¾	99¾	99¾	99¾	**99¾**
Humidity (degrees F., wet bulb)	85-87	83-85	84-86	84-86	86-88	83-85	86-88	83-85	84-86	84-86	80-82	82-86	**84-86**
Do Not Turn Eggs After	19th day	25th day	25th day	31st day	25th day	25th day	21st day	25th day	21st day	15th day	21st day	22nd day	**15th day**
Operating Temperature During Last 3 Days of Incubation (degrees F., dry bulb)	99	98½	98¾	98¾	98½	99	99	98½	99	99	99	99	**99**
Humidity During Last 3 Days of Incubation (degrees F., wet bulb)	90-94	90-94	90-94	90-94	[3]90-94	90-94	92-95	90-94	90-94	90-94	90-94	90-94	**90-94**
Open Ventilation Holes One-Fourth	10th day	14th day	12th day	15th day	1st day	14th day	12th day	14th day	12th day	8th day	12th day	12th day	**8th day**
Open Ventilation Holes Further if Needed To Control Temperature	18th day	25th day	25th day	30th day	25th day	24th day	20th day	25th day	20th day	14th day	20th day	21st day	**14th day**

[1] It has been reported that duck eggs hatch better in still-air incubators than in forced-air incubators.

[2] For still-air incubators add **2-3°F.** to the recommended operating temperatures.

[3] Better hatchability may be obtained if goose eggs are sprinkled with warm water or dipped in lukewarm water for half a minute each day during the last half of the incubation period.

Chart courtesy of Clemson University — Bulletin No. 530

Many abnormalities occur in chicks which have been incubated at temperatures above the optimum. The most common being crooked toes and spraddled legs. High temperatures also affect the proper development of the brain, eyes and head region in general. Normally an embryo will draw the yolk sac and its contents into the body cavity through the naval opening where it serves as food for the chick during the first 72 hours of life. Should the chick hatch before this process is completed they will usually die a few days later.

High temperatures will bring about premature drying of the emerging chicks causing them to stick in the shell, thus preventing the chick from hatching.

To prevent overheating after hatching it may be necessary to remove chicks from the trays and place them in boxes several times during the hatching process.

When incubation temperatures are below optimum, hatches are late and slow. Characteristically, embryos will be alive at the end of the normal incubation period but only a few eggs will be pipped. Some early mortality will accompany late hatches.

Embryonic development is a step by step process, which means there is a definite timetable for the development of each part of the chick's body. The head formation begins on the first day of incubation; the heart starts to beat on the second. After 72 hours the leg and wing buds make an appearance and so on. Low incubation temperatures will cause a deformity in the body section under development at the time the heat deficiency occurs. That is, if the heat drops below optimum level on the fourth (4th) day of incubation most likely the chick's mouth or tongue will be deformed. The developing embryo must have the proper amount of heat at all times. Temperatures above the optimum will not balance a heat deficiency at some other time.

Incubation temperatures not only regulate and determine time of hatch but also plays a vital part in the quality of the chick you produce.

THE ORDER OF PECK!

Did you know there is a "Society" of family life in a flock of chickens? A limited few rule the "ROOST- they are in charge, so to speak. Some dominate at the feeders and fountains. Professor A. M. Guhl of Kansas State University of Manhattan, Kansas, conducted considerable research on this subject. The most notable reporting was an illustrated article in Life Magazine of August 2, 1948 titled "The Social Order of Hens". A rigid hierarchy among all chickens is determined simply by the problem of who can peck whom.

Humidity

Nature provides that eggs should dry out to some extent during incubation due to evaporation. The speed at which these eggs lose moisture will depend on four factors: altitude (air pressure), relative humidity of the surrounding air, temperature and ventilation rate.

Everything being equal, evaporation will occur faster at higher altitudes, in drier air (lower relative humidity) at higher temperatures and in faster moving air (ventilation).

The normal fluid loss should be about 11% of the original egg weight. As the egg loses moisture the air cell increases in volume, thus air cell size can be a guide to proper humidity control. See Diagram. Candle eggs to check enlargment of the air cell on the 7th, 14th and 18th day of incubation. If the size exceeds the relative depth indicated in diagram 2, the humidity is too low and the surface area of the water pan should be increased. If the relative depth is less than the size indicated in the diagram, the humidity is too high and the size of the water pan should be reduced.

Removing the eggs from the incubator for candling does little harm if you handle them gently. It may slow up development of the chick, though, depending upon how much the egg is cooled. Generally, if the eggs are removed from the incubator two or three times for a PERIOD OF NO MORE THAN 15 MINUTES EACH, SUCH COOLING WILL MAKE LITTLE DIFFERENCE IN THE TOTAL INCUBATION TIME REQUIRED FOR HATCHING.

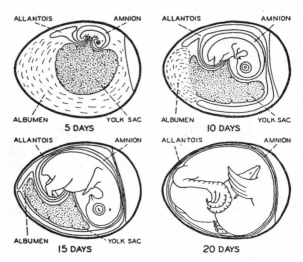

IMPORTANT EVENTS IN EMBRYONIC DEVELOPMENT
(From A. L. Romanoff — Cornell Rural School Leaflet, September 1939.)

Operators must have a method of measuring the evaporation rate in order to determine the humidity level. The easiest method of estimating the humidity is to compare the dry and wet bulb thermometer.

The bulb of a wet bulb thermometer is encased in a round wick-like sock. The other end of the sock is placed in a reservoir of water. Due to capillary action the material will remain permanently damp. Through evaporation the sock loses moisture to the surrounding air thus cooling the bulb and causing the wet-bulb thermometer reading to be lower than the dry-bulb thermometer. When the air is completely saturated and there is no evaporation from the sock both temperature readings will be the same. On the other hand, the drier the air the greater the evaporation rate and the lower the wet bulb thermometer reading will be, because of the increased cooling brought about by the higher rate of evaporation.

According to Mr. John Wunderlich, a well-known APA poultry judge, many people operating incubators never give any thought to the wick of the hygrometer and how important it is in helping them to get a good hatch. Hygrometer wicks can vary in the type of material used. Some are made of a heavier, more tightly knit material. Others are lighter and thinner. Judge Wunderlich recommends using this lighter wick for a more precise reading.

The ideal moisture level is about 50-55% relative humidity (83-87°F on a wet bulb thermometer) for the first 18 days and about 65% (89-90°F wet bulb) for the last 3 days. Excessive drying because of low humidity will cause the chick to stick to the shell and fail to survive. Some variation above and below the ideal level usually will not affect hatchability drastically.

Again, we point out that it is very important that you follow the manufacturer's instructions in regard to humidity.

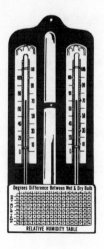

Two popular types of hygrometers that accurately keep a check on humidity.

VERY IMPORTANT

We will give some recommendation for the control of humidity in different types of incubators. Remember, first of all, to follow the manufacturer's instructions. In still-air or sectional incubators the eggs shouldn't be set until moisture level is established in the incubator. Provide sufficient water pan surface to keep the moisture at the proper level. At hatching time provide additional moisture by increasing the water pan surface by adding sponges or other objects to increase evaporating surface. If it is necessary use a spray to add additional moisture at frequent intervals. If the chicks pip the shell but can't get out, add additional moisture even if the moisture is already high.

In a forced draft incubator you shouldn't increase your moisture level until the eggs are transferred to hatching trays. Do not wait for the increase in moisture which comes when the eggs pip. This procedure will cause mortality of embryos in the eggs that pip early because many of the chicks will stick in the shell.

Where a separate hatcher is used you should raise your humidity to the hatching level on the day the eggs are transferred, the 18th for chicken eggs, the 24th for turkey eggs. When chicks are removed during hatching, be certain the humidity returns to the proper level quickly.

When you refill the water pan, use warm water. Hot or cold water will affect the temperature of the incubator too much. To increase the humidity level the last three days, set an extra pan of water in the incubator, or you can put a wet sponge in the incubator to raise the humidity. A word of caution: Do not let the eggs come into direct contact with the water at any time.

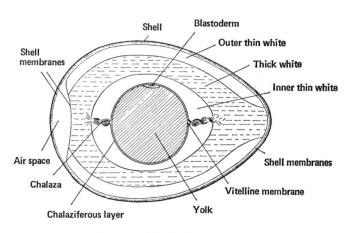

Structure of the fertile egg

Ventilation

Ventilation refers to the air movement or air exchange within the incubator. Proper ventilation is very important during the incubation process. While the embryo is developing, oxygen enters the egg through the shell, and carbon dioxide escapes in the same manner. Proper ventilation serves three important functions. It provides the developing embryo with fresh oxygen, removes carbon dioxide and other gases produced by embryo's digestion of the yolk, and it helps to cool the eggs by removing the heat.

There is no danger of supplying too much oxygen or removing too much carbon dioxide. The problem is that excessive ventilation will reduce both incubator temperature and humidity.

Some vents or air openings must remain open at all times. However, vents should be adjusted to maintain the proper temperature and humidity. As the chicks begin to hatch, it is essential that they receive an increasing supply of oxygen and heat. This means that the air openings need to be opened gradually to increase the flow of air. It may be necessary to increase the size of the water pans at this time in order to maintain the proper level of humidity.

A small amount of carbon dioxide (CO_2) should be present in the surrounding air to stimulate embryo growth. This is especially important during the first 72 hours of incubation. Some manufacturers recommend that the top vents be closed on their machines during the first 3 days of incubation. Research has shown that a CO_2 level of .4% promotes excellent embryonic growth. When CO_2 reached the 1.0% level or higher, growth was depressed and embryonic mortality increased. Normally, the atmosphere contains 21.0% oxygen and 0.04% carbon dioxide with the remainder being nitrogen.

Care should be exercised in selecting a site for your incubator. Locate your incubator in a room in which the temperature is between 70° and 75°F, and which is free from drafts and excessive variations in temperature. Do not place the incubator near windows where it will be exposed to the direct rays of the sun. The sun's rays may raise the temperature so much that all of the embryos will be destroyed. Incubators placed against a wall or in a corner, or dead air space may give poor results due to the lack of proper ventilation

An oxygen deficiency will cause chicks to pant, chirp and scurry around the hatching tray. A shortage of this life sustaining gas will cause an enlargement of the blood vessels of the lung. Also the vessels will take on the dark color associated with cyanosis or oxygen starvation. Oxygen deprivation may decrease hatchability, reduce growth and prevent the development of a normal circulatory system.

In an attempt to determine when oxygen is most critical to the developing chick, a newly hatched chick, a pipped egg and a hatching egg in which the fully developed embryo had not yet punctured the shell were all placed in a sealed container. The newly hatched chick was the first to die, followed by the pipped chick and then the non-pipped embryo. This would indicate that newly hatched chickens have a higher oxygen requirement than does the embryo which is still encased in the shell.

Many times poor hatches experienced by poultrymen living in mountain areas are due to the lower oxygen content of the atmosphere at these higher altitudes. There hatcherymen may experience some problems when they received hatching eggs produced at lower altitudes.

From the standpoint of ventilation there are two classes of incubators — still-air or gravity circulation and forced-draft. Still-air or gravity circulation machines are based on the principal that warm air is lighter than cool air and will rise to the top of the machine and escape through the upper vents. Forced-draft or forced-circulation incubators employ a fan to insure an even distribution of warm air throughout the machine. Because the air is the same temperature anywhere in the machine, many layers of eggs can be incubated, at the same time, this is not true of a still-air machine.

A Well Ventilated, Clean Room for Incubation is VERY IMPORTANT!

Power Failure

If there's a power failure, we suggest you place your incubator in a warm room next to a hot radiator or hot air vent. Don't over compensate by raising the temperature too high. Also hot water bottles can be placed on top of the eggs.

If you have a small incubator put the eggs in cake pans and place them in a warm oven. Watch the temperature closely so as not to overheat them and add moisture.

If you have a forced air incubator close the air vent. For a period of time you will have to watch and make sure you haven't added too much heat.

If it is at all possible, rush your incubator to an area where electrical power is available. Seek out a small generator plant. Where a large number of eggs are at stake, it is wise to have your own stand-by generator.

A Checklist of Steps to Watch During Incubation

1. Study the incubator manufacturer's directions FREQUENTLY since failure to observe the proper rules of operation may result in poor hatches.

2. Check thermometers and electrical controls well before the beginning of each hatch. A clinical thermometer should be used to check the accuracy of the incubator thermometers.

3. Rinse the wicks of the wet-bulb thermometer daily and wash them with soap once each week. Dirty wicks cause faulty wet-bulb readings.

4. Always keep complete records of incubator operation including: wet-bulb and dry-bulb temperature, time, direction of turkey, adjustments, and other pertinent information. Such records may be helpful in determining the possible cause of poor hatches or may make it possible to duplicate good hatching conditions.

5. Keep spare wicks, pilot lights, wafers, microswitches and other parts on hand at ALL times.

THE QUALITY JOURNEY OF AN EGG

MARKET EGG QUALITY —

GOING

AA Quality

GOING

A Quality

QUALITY HILL

HATCHING EGGS VERY SIMILAR

B Quality

GOING

C Quality

GONE Inedible

Is perishable.
Is finest when first laid.
Starts its journey at once.
Makes the journey quickly in HIGH and slowly in LOW temperature.
At home or market depends on HOLDING CONDITIONS.

Any Egg is Somewhere on Quality Hill - Its Condition and Appearance Tell Where.
Prompt - Proper Cooling Can Help Greatly

SANITATION PROCEDURES

The following sanitation procedures are quite comprehensive. Many of the suggestions are just common sense sanitary habits. Some of the more detailed procedures are obviously intended for the larger scale operations.

Hatching Egg Sanitation

Hatching eggs should be collected from the nests at frequent intervals and to aid in the prevention of contamination with disease causing organism, the following practices should be observed:

(a) Cleaned and disinfected containers should be used in collecting the eggs, and precautions taken to prevent contamination from organisms that may be present on the hands or clothing of the person making the collection.

(b) Dirty eggs should not be used for hatching purposes and should be collected in a separate container from hatching eggs. Slightly soiled eggs may be dry cleaned by hand or motor driven buffer.

(c) The visibly clean eggs should be fumigated as soon as possible after collection.

(d) The fumigated eggs should be stored in a cool place. Eggs should be stored no longer than necessary before setting. Racks used for storing eggs should be properly cleaned and disinfected.

(e) New or clean, fumigated cases should be used to transport eggs to the hatchery. Soiled egg case fillers should be destroyed.

Hatching Room Sanitation

An effective program for the prevention and control of infections should include the following measures:

(a) The hatching room should be situated so that it's completely removed from the breeding stock.

(b) The equipment should be kept clean and sanitary conditions maintained.

(c) Only clean eggs should be used for hatching purposes. All eggs set should be fumigated prior to setting or as soon as possible (preferably within 12 hours) after they are placed in the incubator. They should also be fumigated after transfer to a separate hatcher.

(d) Only new or clean, fumigated egg cases should be used for transportation of hatching eggs. Soiled egg case fillers should be destroyed.

(f) Newly hatched chicks, ducklings, goslings or other poultry should be placed into clean containers. Then, as soon as possible they should be moved to the brooding area.

Cleaning and Disinfecting

The following procedures are recommended:

(a) In the poultry houses, hatchery rooms and delivery trucks:

(1) Settle dust by spraying lightly with the disinfectant to be used.

(2) Remove all litter and droppings to an isolated area where there is no opportunity for dissemination of any infectious disease organisms that may be present.

(3) Scrub the walls, floors, and equipment with a hot soapy water solution. Rinse to remove soap.

(4) Spray with a disinfectant which is registered by the Environmental Protection Agency as germicidal, fungicidal, pseudomonocidal, and tuberculocidal, in accordance with the specifications for use, as shown on the lable of such disinfectant.

(b) In the hatchers:

(1) Follow the manufacturers instructions regarding cleaning of the equipment.

(2) Remove trays and all controls and fans for separate cleaning. The ceiling, walls, and floors should be thoroughly wetted with a stream of water; then scrubbed with a hard bristle brush. Rinse until there is no longer an deposit on the walls, particularly near the fan opening.

(3) Replace the cleaned fans and controls. Replace the trays, preferably still wet from cleaning, and bring the incubator to normal operating temperature.

(4) The hatcher should be fumigated prior to the transfer of the eggs.

(c) If the same machine is used for incubating and hatching, the entire machine should be cleaned after each hatch. A vacuum cleaner should be used to remove dust and down from the egg trays; then the entire machine should be vacuumed, mopped, and fumigated according to recommended procedures.

Fumigation

Fumigation is recommended for sanitizing eggs and hatchery equipment as an essential part of a sanitation program.

(a) Fumigation of clean eggs after collection should be done as follows:

(1) Provide a room or cabinet proportionate to the number of eggs to be handled. The room should be relatively tight and must be equipped with a fan to circulate the air during fumigation and to expel it after fumigation.

(2) The eggs should be placed on wire racks, in wire baskets, or on cup-type egg flats stacked outside of the egg cases (to permit air circulation) and exposed to circulating formaldehyde gas.

(3) Formaldehyde gas is provided by mixing 0.6 gram of potassium permanganate with 1.2 cc. of formalin (37.5 percent) for each cubic foot of space in the room. The ingredients should be mixed in an earthenware or enamelware container having a capacity at least 10 times the volume of the total ingredients.

(4) Circulate the gas within the room for 20 minutes; then expel.

(5) The temperature in the cabinet during fumigation should be at least 70 degrees F., and the relative humidity above 70 percent.

(b) Eggs should be fumigated at the hatchery prior to setting or as soon as possible after setting (preferably within 12 hours). Single or repeated fumigation of eggs in the setter may be practiced, but the fumigation schedule should be such that no eggs are fumigated during the period from the 24th to the 84th hour of incubation. The following procedure should be used:

(1) Determine the size of the incubator by multiplying the length times the width times the height.

(2) After setting the eggs and allowing temperature and humidity to regain normal operating levels, release formaldehyde gas into the incubator.

(3) For each cubic foot of space in the incubator, use 0.4 grams of potassium permanganate and 0.8 cc. of formaling (37.5 percent). For mixing the fumigants, use an earthenware or enamelware container having the capacity of at least 10 times the volume of the total ingredients.

(4) Close vents and doors but keep circulating fan operating, and continue fumigation for 20 minutes with normal operating temperature and humidity.

(5) After 20 minutes of fumigation the vents should be opened to the normal operating positions to release the gas.

(c) Eggs which have not been fumigated in the hatchery as described in paragraph (b) of this section should be fumigated after the 84th hour of incubation. The procedure described in paragraph (b) of this section should be followed.

(d) All eggs should be fumigated after transfer to a separate hatcher, preferably as soon as the temperature and humidity regain normal operating levels. The procedure described in paragraph (b) of this section should be followed.

(e) Empty hatchers should be fumigated between each hatch. After the interior of the hatcher has been thoroughly cleaned and the cleaned trays returned, the following procedure should be followed:

(1) After temperature and humidity are brought to normal operating levels, use 0.6 grams of potassium permanganate and 1.2 cc. of formalin (37.5 percent) per cubic foot of space in the hatcher.

(2) Close the doors and vents and leave closed at least 3 hours, preferably overnight.

(f) The cheesecloth method of fumigation described in the paragraph may be used in lieu of the chemical method described in paragraph (b) of this section, using 0.6 cc. of formalin (37.5 percent) per cubic foot of space in the incubator, or in lieu of the chemical method described in paragraph (e) of this section, using 0.9 cc. of formalin (37.5 percent) for each cubic foot of space in the empty hatcher.

(1) Enough cheesecloth should be used to absorb all of the formalin that is to be used for the fumigation.

(2) The formalin-saturated cheesecloth should be hung in the cabinet in such a manner as to permit the circulating air to evaporate all the formalin. This will require longer than 20 minutes.

(3) Care should be taken to prevent the cheesecloth from blocking the air movement created by the fans.

(4) The cheesecloth method is not suitable for still air machines.

CLEAN DISTILLED WATER
FOR YOUR HYGROMETER

This is advisable for your hygrometer. A dirty hygrometer wick can cause an inaccurate reading.

NATURAL HATCHING

**Courtesy of the Ministry of
Agriculture, Fisheries and Food of England Bulletin 43**

For the small poultry keeper who wants to raise a few chicks, and who does not want the bother and expense of even a small incubator, natural hatching under a broody hen is the ideal way. It is, however, essentially dependent on having a broody or broodies.

It is never wise to assume that an apparently broody hen will sit; it is best, therefore, to give her a few dummy eggs for a start, and only substitute the genuine sitting after two or three days if she shows a real intention to brood. It is always advisable to give her the eggs — dummy or genuine — in the evening, rather than during the day, as this is less likely to put her off sitting.

Preparation of the Nest

If the hen has picked her own nest and it is in a convenient and safe place, she should be left on it. Otherwise, a nest or box should be prepared where it is convenient, and where the hen can be assured of quiet and protection from vermin and weather.

The nest-box should be 14 in. square and at least 16 in. high. The front should be open, but it is advisable to board across the first 4 in. from the ground. If the box is to rest on the ground the bottom should be covered with ½ in. mesh wire netting, which will stop vermin burrowing in but which will still allow the rise of soil moisture to the nest. An indoor box should stand on 2 in. of soil, and the inside should be overlaid with a freshly cut turf, ½ in. larger than the floor dimenstions, which should be placed grass side down, and pressed down to give a shallow saucer-shaped depression. Should the weather be dry, the eggs should be sprayed with warm water several times after the 16th day. The nest-box can be fitted with a drop door, if desired, hinged so that it can fold back on to the top, and of such size that when lowered it covers most of the open front. When a door is fitted, it is necessary to allow for additional ventilation by boring a number of 1 in. holes in the back and sides ½ in. from the top.

The nest should be lined with clean, short straw or hay, and should be dusted liberally with a reliable insecticide powder. Fresh litter should be used and the nest-box thoroughly cleaned after each hatch. A treatment with creosote immediately after each hatching season will help to preserve the box.

Feeding and Exercise

During the first seventeen days the hen should come off the nest at least once a day, to allow stretching the legs and emptying the bowels without fouling the nest or eggs. As the hen is a creature of habit, it is a good plan to combine the daily run with feeding routine. It is necessary to make this combined exercise and feeding at a regular time, for the hen may get restless if her normal time has passed. She should be allowed back to the nest after twenty minutes, except in very cold weather when the time can be shortened. The short absence from the nest also helps to aerate the eggs.

Most hens will come off the nest to feed of their own free will but some may have to be lifted off, and the sitting bird must be handled very carefully. First, the wings should be raised gently to release any eggs that may be held between the wings and body; failure to do this may result in broken eggs and a messy nest. When it is certain that no eggs are held between wings and body, the hen may be lifted with one hand under the body and the other over her back. The hen should always be lifted from or returned to the nest head first to reduce her tendency to resist, and to prevent the wings getting caught up in the sides of the entrance.

Testing the Eggs

Unless the tester is experienced, it is better to delay the first testing of eggs until the ninth day, when all clear eggs should be removed. Eggs should be tested again at the fifteenth or sixteenth day, and any dead-in-shell removed.

The simplest apparatus for testing hatching eggs consists of a small box, 9 in. deep, blacked on the inside, and with an egg-shaped hole slightly smaller than an egg cut in the bottom. This box is inverted over a forty-watt electric bulb in a darkened room.

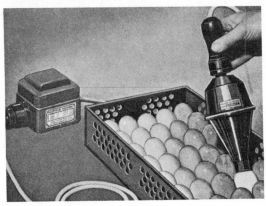

Before testing any sitting of eggs during incubation, it is advisable for a beginner to test a few new-laid eggs over the lamp. A new-laid egg placed over the hole should allow light to penetrate the shell and albumen, so that only the yolk shows up as a faint shadow. At any testing, eggs having this appearance should be removed as infertile. They need not be thrown away as they are quite suitable for cake or pastry making, even after they have been underneath the hen for nine days.

A fertile egg at the ninth day will show a distinctive pattern, with a fine network of veins running out from a dark center. This pattern gets darker and more solid as time goes on. The air space at the broad end is the only part to show clear at this stage. An addled egg will show a cloudy and spotted appearance.

At the fifteenth or sixteenth day the evidence of embryonic life should be the presence of large blood vessels near the air cell, and a large dark shape that will often show movement. Eggs with a dark center, but a clear area round the edges, probably contain dead embryo. If a beginner is in doubt such eggs should be specially marked and returned to the nest; subsequent examination at hatching will help to identify the dead-in-shell. With a little practice the number of eggs classed as doubtful will decrease.

Hatching

The hen should not be disturbed after the seventeenth day. The nest-box should be kept open, and food and water left handy each day. Hatching may begin on the twentieth day after sitting, and should be completed within twenty-four hours of the first chick pipping the shell. Chicks hatching later than this seldom do well. It is important to watch the behaviour of the hen rather closely at this time. If she is excitable or vicious, it may be advisable to remove the chicks as they hatch, and keep them in a flannel-lined basket in a warm place until the hatch is complete. The hen may take to the chicks after that. Otherwise they will have to be reared artificially or be given another broody to look after. Some hens will start to mother the first two or three chicks and forget about the other eggs; if this happens, the chicks should be treated as above and returned to the hen when only the last two or three eggs remain to hatch.

As soon as the hatch is finished, the empty shells and any unhatched eggs should be removed from the nest-box; the hen should be given food and water, and then left undisturbed with the chicks for twenty-four hours. Chicks will not need feeding for thirty-six hours after hatching.

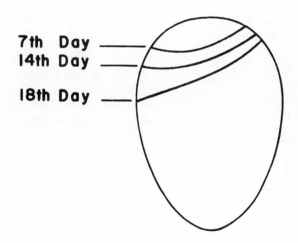

7th Day ———
14th Day ———
18th Day ———

Size of the air cell in the egg on the 7th, 14th, and 18th days of incubation.

ARTIFICIAL INSEMINATION OF POULTRY

J.L. Skinner and L.C. Arrington

A simple method of artificial insemination can improve poultry fertility. Practice and basic knowledge of the chicken's anatomy is all that is necessary.

Chicken breeders may be disappointed when their better birds fail to reproduce. They may not mate because of shyness, physical limitations, lack of purposeful interest or social incompatibility. Unsatisfactory nutrition and age of breeders, management conditions, egg collection and holding practices, and incubation procedures are other possible influences.

If birds do not reproduce when other conditions are adequate, artificial insemination can be the answer. It is a relatively simple procedure used for many kinds of birds, but does require practice and the proper equipment. It cannot, however, overcome poor management practices, genetic lethals or differences, or poor health, nor will it halt early embryonic deaths.

Artificial insemination is more an art than a science. The procedure is not highly technical, but basic knowledge and appreciation of the bird's anatomy is necessary. Success depends considerably on the practice and patience of the inseminator. Wild bird and waterfowl breeders would do well to practice first with some type of common poultry. An excellent choice would be Cornish bantams.

Equipment needed for satisfactory artificial insemination is simple. Figure 1 shows tools that are most frequently used to produce satisfactory results when inseminating a small number of birds. (More complicated equipment — including injection guns, collection aspirators and temperature controlled containers for holding semen — is sometimes employed in large commercial operations.) Figure 2 shows a one-operator stand useful for insemination.

The Male

For satisfactory results, the male used for artificial insemination:

1. Must be mature, in good health, and a physically normal representative of its variety.

2. Must be sexually active. (This is especially important in birds that have a limited season. Light stimulation may be used to control the season in some varieties.)

3. Should be tame, or at least not terrified when restrained or handled.

4. Should be free from external parasites. Some parasites irritate the vent area making male organ exposure both difficult and painful to the bird.

5. Should be kept apart from, but preferably in sight of, the females.

6. Should not be subjected to extremely high temperatures or allowed to become overheated.

Procedure

Experts have developed several methods of holding males for semen collection. Techniques may require either one or two persons. The following 2-operator method works well, resulting in minimum fright or feather damage to the bird.

Hold the male with his head toward the operator and with the keel lying in the palm of the left hand. Secure the **right** leg between the first and second fingers. To make larger birds more comfortable, hold the **left** leg between the second and third fingers. Stroke the back from midpoint toward the tail with the right hand, massaging the abdomen from below with the fingers of the left hand. After several vigorous strokes, transfer the right hand from the back to a position where the thumb and forefinger can apply pressure to either side of the vent. Simultaneously, apply pressure to the abdomen with the fingers of the left hand. This will normally extend the copulatory organ causing a flow of whitish liquid, or semen, as shown in Figure 3. A slight milking action may increase semen flow. An assistant should catch the semen in an eye cup or any other small smooth-edged vessel. In some instances, especially with some waterfowl, the copulatory organ may not extend completely. Semen collection is still possible as it flows over the surface of the partially everted vent.

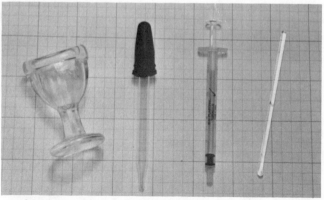

These simple tools — glass eye-cup, medicine dropper, 1 c.c. plastic syringe and glass rod — are all that is needed for artificial insemination of poultry and other birds if an assistant is present.

Points to Remember

● Stimulate males and collect semen immediately after catching. To hold a male, even a relatively tame one, for only a few moments may interfere with collection.

● Successful semen collection is usually the result of an experienced operator and an experienced subject.

● First attempts at "working" inexperienced males often produce disappointing results. Some males pass feces or urates as they discharge semen. Make every effort to collect only the semen; contaminated semen will usually produce poor results. Lessen the chances for contamination by withholding water and feed for 4 to 6 hours prior to collection.

● The volume of semen discharged varies considerably from one bird to another. Most males will produce between .1 cc and .4 cc during each successful collection.

● Individual males vary considerably in the time needed to replenish their semen supply, but normally, collection once every 2 to 4 days is possible without harming the bird.

● Use the semen as soon as possible. It may be held one or two hours without great loss in fertilizing capacity, or for longer periods under controlled conditions. Prevent dehydration and keep the semen temperature below the body temperature of the male that produced it.

The Female

For satisfactory results, the female used in artificial insemination:

1. **Must** be in production or she may be injured.

2. Must not have a hard-shelled egg discernable in the lower portion of the oviduct so that the sperm can move more easily in the area where it unites with the ova.

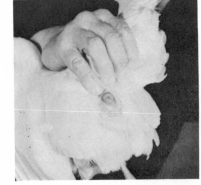

Note position of hands and the exposed terminal end of the oviduct of this female chicken.

Artificial Insemination may be THE ANSWER to YOUR Reproduction Problem.

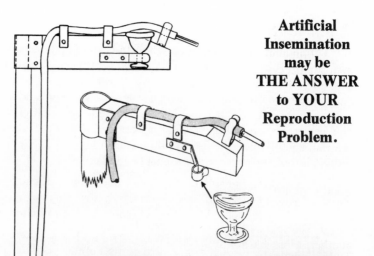

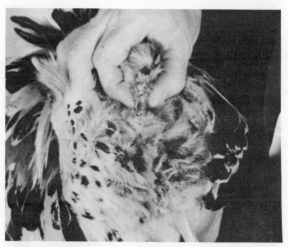

Note position of the operator's right hand. The white area between the thumb and forefinger is the flow of semen of this male chicken.

This stand enables one person to collect semen and place it into the female. The male is held over the eye cup and the semen discharged into it. The exposed oviduct opening of the female is placed over the glass tube which has previously had a quantity of semen placed in it. The operator forces the semen into the oviduct by depressing the rubber bulb with his foot.

Procedure

Throughout the process of handling and exposing the female, remember that the hen is delicate and must be treated gently. Hold and stimulate her much the same way as the male. As the operator applies pressure following the preliminary stroking and massage, the vent will evert and an orifice will appear on the left side. It may be a round rosette or a cleft or skin overfold. This orifice, shown in Figure 4, is the terminal opening of the oviduct. An assistant should place the semen into this opening to a depth of ¼ to 1 inch with a 1 cc syringe, a medicine dropper or similar device.

When making individual matings — one male with one female — use the entire semen collection. Various studies, however, show that good results can be achieved with as little as .05 cc of semen per insemination.

Relax pressure on the female's body as soon as possible after insemination so the oviduct can return to its normal position, drawing the semen inward.

Points to Remember

● The frequency of insemination needed for satisfactory results varies somewhat among females. Insemination may be advisable at more frequent intervals at the onset of production, but once some eggs have been fertilized, once-a-week insemination is sufficient to maintain a satisfactory level.

● Fertile eggs will normally be obtained from 48 to 96 hours following insemination and up to three weeks thereafter. The percentage of fertile eggs from a flock will begin to drop in 5 to 7 days and usually will be unsatisfactory beyond 10 days.

● Turkeys will remain fertile longer than some other birds. Geese show considerable individual variation.

Professor John Skinner has given many demonstrations teaching Artificial Insemination. To observe first hand aids the learning process. However, with some practice you can learn it by diligently following out these directions. Each step is very important to attain successful insemination.

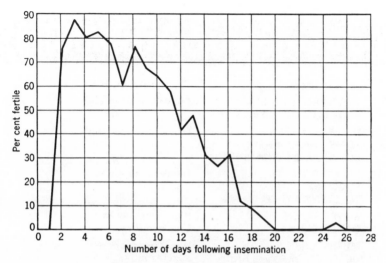

Duration of fertility after artificial insemination of hens. Courtesy Missouri Agr. Expt. Sta.

INCUBATION TROUBLE SHOOTER

Symptoms	Probable Causes
1. HATCHING TOO EARLY WITH BLOODY NAVELS	Temperature too high
2. DRAGGY HATCH SOME CHICKS EARLY, BUT SLOW IN FINISHING	Temperature too high
3. DELAYED HATCH EGGS NOT PIPPING UNTIL 21ST DAY, OR LATER	Temperature too low
4. SHORT DOWN ON CHICKS	High temperature Low Humidity
5. MUSHY CHICKS DEAD ON TRAYS — BAD ODOR	Navel infection, and remains in incubator
6. CHICKS TOO SMALL	Low humidity High Temperature
7. STICKY CHICKS SHELL STICKING TO CHICKS	Eggs dried down too much. Low humidity at hatching time
8. STICKY CHICKS CHICKS SMEARED WITH EGG CONTENTS	Low average temperature. Humidity may be too high
9. CRIPPLED CHICKS MISSING EYE CROSS BEAK EXTRA LEG, ETC.	Mostly chance Heredity in some cases Also temperature
10. ROUGH NAVELS	High temperature Low Humidity

INCUBATION PERIODS

Below are the number of days it takes for eggs of the various classes of poultry to hatch:

Hen	21 days	Guinea	26-28 days
Duck	28 days	Pheasant	21-24 days
Duck (Muscovy)	35-37 days	Pea fowl	28 days
Goose	28-32 days	Ostrich	42 days
Turkey	28 days	Pigeon	18 days

INCUBATION TROUBLE SHOOTING CHART

Symptoms	Probable causes	Suggestions
Many clear eggs. No blood. (Determined by candling, then broken out appearance.)	1. Infertility. Too many males, too inactive, or frozen combs and wattles. 2. Embryo died early 1-2 days.	1. Use young, vigorous males. Do not hold eggs longer than 7 days. Keep at temperature of 50°-55° F., in moist atmosphere. Gather often. 2. Check accuracy of thermometer. Check termostat, heating element, current supply. Check operating temperature against instructions.
Slight blood rings	3. a. Improper temperature. b. Fumigation. 4. Improper care of eggs before setting.	3. a. Check accuracy of thermometer. Check termostat, heating element, current supply. Check operating temperature against instructions. b. Do not fumigate at high concentrations during the first 5 days of age. 4. See suggestions (2) above.
Many dead germs	5. Temperature too high or too low. 6. Improper turning of eggs. 7. Improper feeding of flock. 8. Breeding (low hatchability inherited.) 9. Improper ventilation; insufficient oxygen.	5. See suggestions (3) above. 6. Turn at least 3 times, preferably 5 in 24 hours. 7. See (3) above. 8. Check vitamin and mineral content of breeder mash. 9. Avoid close inbreeding. Increase ventilation of incubator and incubator rooms, avoid drafts.
Pipped eggs not hatching. Hatch non-uniform. Hatching too early. Hatching too late. Sticky hatch.	10. Insufficient moisture. 11. Too high temperature. 12. Too low temperature. 13. Probably too high temperature.	10. Increase evaporating surface for moisture. First 18 days wet bulb of 85°-87° F., 3 day hatching period 88°-90° F. 11. See (3) above. 12. See (3) above. 13. See (3) above.
Cripples and malpositions	14. Temperature too high. 15. Too low moisture. 16. Improper turning or setting. 17. Hatching trays too smooth.	14. See (3) above. 15. See (10) above. 16. See (6) above. Set eggs large end up. 17. Use wire bottom trays or crinoline.
*Very large, soft-bodied, weak chicks. Mushy chicks. Dead on trays, bad odor.	18. Low average temperature. 19. Poor ventilation. 20. Navel infection in incubator.	18. See (3) above. 19. See (9) above. 20. Careful cleaning and fumigation of incubator between hatches.
Rough navels	21. High temperature or wide temperature variations. 22. Low moisture.	21. See (3) above. 22. See (10) above.

*Does not include "big bones" slightly "green" chicks resulting from high moisture since these chicks will live and ship well.

UNIVERSITY OF KENTUCKY: AGRICULTURAL EXPERIMENT STATION, POULTRY SECTION—

LEAHY CHART FOR LOCATING INCUBATION PROBLEMS

Condition of Eggs	GENERAL REASONS	SUGGESTED CORRECTIONS
Clear and un-developed eggs.	1. Interference while birds are mating. 2. Holding eggs too long. 3. Too many hens to the rooster.	1. Fence off breeding stock so no unauthorized people will bother your breeders. 2. For better results, set eggs within 1-7 days after laying. Hold eggs in room temperature 40 to 60 degrees. 3. Change hens to other roosters, if not mating. Use artificial breeding.
Clear egg with blood ring or slightly de-veloped.	1. Eggs have been heated or chilled before placed in incubator. 2. Incubator temperature too irregular.	1. Place eggs in even temperature if possible for storage. Have shipper give proper instructions to shipping agency to handle eggs properly. 2. Check your incubators frequently for proper temperature.
Dead germ or Embryo when egg is broken to check.	1. Eggs held too long before setting. 2. Wide temperature variation. 3. Improper turning. 4. Improper feeding. 5. Extensive inbreeding.	1-2. Same as in box 2 for care and setting. 3. Eggs must be turned at least 3 times daily. Eggs should be turned within an eight hour period. 4. If information is not available, use different feeds to parts of breeding flock divided off in sections. Mark eggs from each section. Use feed for flock, which is being used in the better producing section. 5. Where inbreeding is extensive, obtain new breeding stock. Discard old breeders.
Eggs pipping but not com-pleting hatch. Dead in shell.	1. Too much moisture. Chick too large in shell to work out. 2. Not enough moisture. Chick unable to reach air cell to pip shell.	1. Open air vents to reduce high moisture reading during incubation. 2. Increase moisture reading to retard drying down too fast. Follow manufacturers instructions. Check eggs periodically for size of air cell.
Early hatches	1. Too high temperature maintained during entire hatch.	1. If there is as much as a degree and a half variation in your dry bulb reading, set the correct reading midway between the high and low reading. Use temperature recommended by manufacturer.
Late hatch	1. Too low temperature maintained during entire hatch. 2. Old eggs.	1. Same as for early hatch. 2. Proper care should be given the eggs.
Crippled and deformed chicks.	1. Temperature maintain-ed too low. 2. Improper turning. 3. Eggs not placed properly in tray.	1. Maintain proper temperature during hatch. 2. Follow turning instructions as above. 3. Place all eggs with small or pointed end down, unless specified by manufacturer. Use proper egg positioners if obtainable.

For a better hatch of eggs and chicks with more vigor and vitality, increase moisture to proper reading when through turning eggs and hatching period started. Also, when eggs are being pipped, reduce your dry thermometer reading 1 degree.

HUMIDAIRE TROUBLE SHOOTER
CHECK LIST
(Forced Air Incubator)

1. Check line voltage — by 24-hour test recording volt meter.

2. Check fans for lubrication — front and rear bearings.

3. Check instruments — Hygrometer and Thermometer.

4. Do not run forced draft incubators over 100°F. Any temperature over 100°F is killing to the developing embryo.

5. Do not remove water from water tanks. Look to other adjustments.

6. Must have room ventilation to permit carbon dioxide to escape and oxygen to enter.

7. Ammonia fumes killing to the embryo. This is caused by insufficient ventilation in room, chick dropping and plain filth.

8. Do you have your Hygrometer properly connected? See sketch.

9. Have your eggs been trayed properly? All eggs should be placed small end down, large end up — except Goose eggs.

10. 2 oz. egg basis for incubator capacity.

11. Proper ventilation is window open about 2 inches with baffle board or muslin to direct air current with no drafts. Provide an opening in center of ceiling to allow foul air to be expelled.

12. If incubator turns one way but not in the other direction, your trouble is your time switch not making proper contact, or, your clock points are not making contact.

13. Check all electrical connections to see that they are all tight.

A Louse is a Louse!
For they can really Louse up
Your Hatches!

No fowl can concentrate on their mating and laying eggs with a frustrating lot of lice "playing tag" all over their bodies! Owls, wild animals, rats, cats even children playing in the poultry yard, can cause disturbances that interfere with mating and disturb the hens on the nests, which will hurt hatchability.

LITTLE KNOWN HISTORICAL POULTRY FACTS OF INTEREST

Quoted in Genesis, Chapter One of the Old Testament we learn of the very start of what centuries later would be such an important part to our every day living, the producing, together with the need for meat and eggs. In the Beginning when God created the Earth, Man, all Things and Beings, it was on the 5th day He created the fish and fowl. He blessed them saying: "Be fruitful and multiply and fill the waters in the seas, and let the fowl multiply on the Earth." Thus, for those who wonder or joke about which came first, the chicken or the egg, the origin in the Bible completely clarifies it.

Red Jungle Fowl, parent stock of most domestic chickens.

Right: An artist's conception of the ingenius Egyptian incubators. Eggs were incubated in the lower compartment and fuel above so the fumes could be exhausted.

For more than 5000 years domestic fowl dates back to 3341 B.C. when a Chinese Emperor Fu-Hsi taught his people how to domesticate the wild fowl for meat and eggs. Even before then, they were domesticated, but for another purpose, which was cock-fighting — a favorite pastime of native Princes of India. Our present day fowl, authorities seem to agree, descended from the Red Jungle Fowl (Gallus Bankiva) still to be found in Burma, Northern India and the Philippines. Of all the present day fowl the Langshan is the oldest known in history. Langshans are the descendants of the Assel or Malay Fowl being traced back to 3000 years ago.

The modern breeds of today for the greater part were primarily bred, developed and populated in the agricultural countries of Europe along with the United States during the 19th century as poultry history verifies. The needs of the people, their fancies and interests have brought about a revolutionary development in chickens during the last 100 years.

To expand the poultry needs of people, it was found the old Mother Hen could not hatch enough chicks. Thereby came the need for artificial incubation. This was known to have taken place, as written by Aristotle in Egypt, as early as 400 B.C. The first incubation was crude, the eggs being hatched in piles of decomposing manure. In 1875 this very same principle was granted a U.S. Patent. The Chinese artificially incubated eggs as early as the period of 246-207 B.C. These ancient incubators were heated with a variety of fuel — dung, straw and charcoal prevailing though other fuels were no doubt used. One writer has stated the Egyptians should be known for their incubators more so than their pyramids. Incubators of a design used at the time of Moses when as many as 15,000,000 to 20,000,000 chicks were hatched in the Land of the Nile — are still in use today. Their construction was of a mud brick much like a kiln or oven as they are often referred to. The exactness of the temperature was tested by holding an egg to their eye lid, so precise was their training, handed down from one generation to the next.

What is equally marvelous is that the Egyptian hatchery was operated on a "toll" or custom hatching basis, the operators getting all chicks left over after he supplied the supplier or egg producer with two chicks for each three eggs brought in. Hatches of 80% up to 87% were known then. On this basis our modern incubators have only shown improvement in hatches over previous mammoth incubators, manufactured during the past 30 years. The most noteworthy accomplishment in view of these historical facts is that so many more chicks are now hatched with so much less labor. Equally astounding is the fact that today in China and Egypt these ancient incubators are still in use. Somewhere in their use the Chinese discovered the use of animal heat, involving the principle of the heat transfer system. Just when this was discovered we have not been able to establish but very briefly the system is as follows: A heavy walled "building" is used often constructed of mud brick walls so they could be termed as insulated though most of the hatcheries were in warmer climates but some are known to have been in North China. Each unit referred to as a "cell" in this incubation room is a basket containing the eggs surrounded by rice hulls with a similar arrangement as ice cream containers in a freezer. To start the incubation cycle the rice hulls are pre-heated the first week. Then the first eggs in muslin bags are placed in the baskets (cells), the dates being marked on a few eggs as to when they were placed in their respective cells — to identify them. Eggs are candled on the 3rd day, the infertiles being sold to bakeries, a practice that is illegal in this country.

In a week, another bag of eggs is placed in each cell, during which time the first eggs are generating some animal heat. Shifting these bags of eggs periodically is their method of turning. These Chinese work about 15 hours per day shifting eggs. At the end of two weeks additional bags of eggs are started. Naturally, with more eggs in this basket the animal heat has increased considerably so that no additional "outside" heat is required. Three ages of eggs are in each cell at all times excepting at the start or finish of the incubation season. Eggs in the basket due to hatch are removed at 14 to 16 days depending on the weather, to a hatching area where no outside heat is supplied though at times they are covered with a blanket. The only modern invention used in these Chinese incubators are electric lights to this very day for even the temperature is checked by placing an egg to their eye lids. Temperature adjustments can be made by air openings covered by curtains, all hand manipulated. One can't help from marvelling at the skill and persistence of these Chinese.

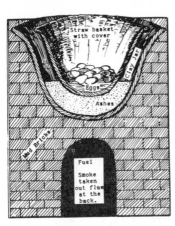

Cross section view of an ancient Chinese incubator.

An artists impression of ancient hatching by body heat about a man's waist in the Orient.

Early hatching in the Philippines by a Tagal native. Eggs were held in between rows of sticks by ashes, covered by several blankets and kept warm by their servants.

Back through the ages incubation of eggs by humans has been known to take place. The primary reasons for this was lack of fuel (money for fuel), no setting hens, no incubators or an emergency. It is doubtful if incubation by humans was very extensive. Emergencies have accounted for numerous instances of incubating by body heat where the Mother Hen died. Such cases have not been limited to ancient times for as recently as January, 1955 a news item from New Zealand reported of George McMillan—" the human hen". As quoted in Time Magazine May 1951, during the lush days of the ostrich feather trade in South Africa when there was a terrific demand for these fine plumes to adorn ladies finery, native girls took turns incubating eggs, to help meet the demand. An amusing aspect in gathering these facts is the reference to wives assigning their lazy husbands the task to hatch out eggs. Roman history reveals the story of Livia Augusta the Empress, wife of Tiberius Claudius Nero (an officer under Julius Caesar) who hatched a cockerel from an egg placed in her bosom foretelling the fact she was to bear a boy. From a German book published in 1787 tells a similar story of Gypsy fortune tellers foretelling the sex of a mother's expected child by having her incubate an egg in her bosom, using this incident to their own advantage in trying to convince skeptics of their trustworthiness. If the egg produced a pullet, the mother would bear a daughter. Or, if the egg hatched a cockerel, she would bear a son. Another interesting story is of the over imbibing drunkard of Syracuse who hatched some eggs buried in the ground, covering them while in his stupor. In the Philippine area back in 1854 the unusually large population of ducks raised by the native Tagals caused wonderment by the explorers. On investigation they found patient servants who served as hatchers. From the historical description an artist conveys a picture of the likely arrangement. Incubation by body heat is a crude possibility but we are sure that few of us could exercise that much patience.

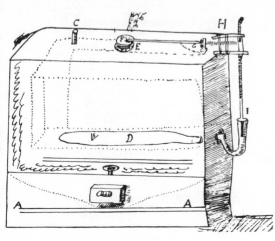

Drebel's incubator with mercury-alcohol thermostat. Credited to an early manuscript in the University Library of Cambridge. England.

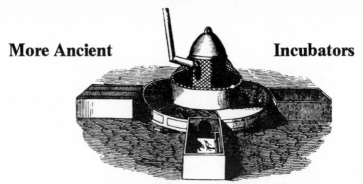

REAUMUR'S HATCHING APPARATUS.

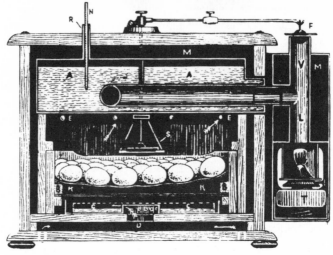

SECTION OF HEARSON'S HOT WATER INCUBATOR

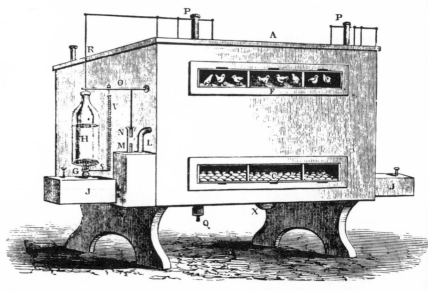

SOURCES OF EQUIPMENT

Artificial Insemination Tubes:

Lorenz Enterprises, 2821 Rodney Avenue, Modesto, California 95351

Teel Plastics Co., Inc. 426 Hitchcock, Baraboo, Wisconsin 53913

Continental Plastics, Inc., Darien, Wisconsin 53114

Stromberg's Chicks & Pets Unlimited, Box 717, Fort Dodge, Iowa 50501

Incubator Companies:

Leahy Incubator Co., Higginsville, Missouri 64037

Marsh Manufacturing Co., 14232 Brookhurst Street, Garden Grove, California 92640

G Q F Manufacturing Co., Box 152, Savannah, Georgia 31402

Petersime Incubator Co., Gettysburg, Ohio

Humidaire Incubator Co., New Madison, Ohio 45346

Brower Manufacturing Co., Quincy, Illinois 62301

Multiple Incubator Co., Sidney, Australia

Redmon Industries, Box 632, Roswell, New Mexico 88201

Oak Ridge Manufacturing Co., Box 99 . . . Veyo Route, Central, Utah 84722

James Landrum Company, Box 117, Baldwyn, Mississippi 38824

Lyon Electric Co., Box 81303, San Diego, California 92138

Jamesway Mfg. Co., Fort Atkinson, Wisconsin 53538

Kuhl Poultry Equipment Co., Flemington, New Jersey 08822

Robbins Incubator Company, Denver, Colorado 80201

Chickmaster Incubator Co., Cleveland, Ohio 44104

Buckeye Incubator Co., (part of Bordon Johnson Industries) Kansas City, Missouri 64101

Stromberg's Chicks & Pets Unlimited, Box 717, Fort Dodge, Iowa 50501

MIXED EGG SETTINGS
ARE NOT ADVISABLE

Setting guinea eggs with goose eggs, for example, is most unwise. Many may not have a choice, however, it can be done. You cannot expect good hatches when doing so.

HATCHING TIME TABLE

DAYS	TYPE OF FOWL
14	Canary; Finch; Dove; Mynah
14-15	Harlequin
16	QUAIL: Button, Cape
17-18	Japanese Quail
18	Rosella; Parakeet; Ceylon Jungle Fowl; Palawan Pheasant; Crested Dove
18-19	Chinese Bamboo Partridge; Pigeon
19	Tinamous; QUAIL: Jungle Bush, Painted Bush, Swamp
20-21	Sonnerat's Junglefowl; Black Indian Francolin
21	QUAIL: Bobwhite, Red; SPURFOWL: Painted, Red; Green Junglefowl; FRANCOLINS: Coqui, Sharpe's, Bare Throated, Crested, Close-barred, Heuglins, Red-winged, Painted, Yellow-necked, Hildebrandt's, Kirk's, Double-spurred; Cocatiel; Germain's Pheasant, Chicken
21-22	Valley Quail; Stone Partridge; Red Junglefowl; FRANCOLINE: Erkel's, Grey Indian
22	QUAIL: Douglas, Gambel; King Eider Duck
22-23	Ceylon Spurfowl
23	Old Squaw Duck; GEESE: Ross's, Black Brant; PARTRIDGE: French Red-Leg, Barbary, Chukar; Ruffed Grouse; QUAIL: Chestnut, Bellied Scale, Blue Scale, Colombian, Crested, Masked Bobwhite
23-24	PHEASANTS: Amherst, Golden
24	White Eared Pheasant; Cockatoos; Lovebirds; GROUSE: Blue, Sharptailed; QUAIL: Mearns, Mountain; Hungarian Partridge; DUCKS: Chilean Pintail, Garganey, Ringed Teal, Spectacled Eider, Ruddy
24½	Ringneck Pheasant
24-25	PHEASANTS: Swinehole, Nepal, W.C. & other Kalij, Mutant, Elliot's, Firebacks, Reeves, Imperial, Mongolian, Blackneck, Formosan, Edwards
25	Vulterine Guinea; DUCKS: Hottentot Teal, Green-winged Teal; Sage Grouse; GEESE: Lesser White-fronted, Snow, Emperor, Red-breasted

HATCHING TIME TABLE

DAYS	TYPE OF FOWL

25-26   Prairie Chicken Grouse

25-27   Chachalacas

25-28   Humes Pheasant

26   GEESE: European White-fronted; Congo Peacock; DUCKS: Philippine, Australian Gray Teal, Chestnut-breasted Teal, Marbled Teal, Cape Teal, Puna Teal, Northern Pintail, Red-billed Pintail, Bahama Pintail, Kerguelen Pintail, Barkal Teal, Chilean Teal, Sharp Wing Gadwall, Falcated Teal, European Widgeon, American Widgeon, Chiloe Widgeon, Blue-winged Teal, Cinnamon Teal, Cape Shoveller, New Zealand Shoveller, Common Shoveller, Southern Pochard, Canvasback, Common White-eye, Australian White-eye, Tufted, Kingneck, New Zealand Scaup, Brazilian Teal

26-27   PHEASANTS: Silver, Linneated Kaliz

27   DUCKS: North American Black Duck, Yellowbills, European Eider, European Pochard, Baer's Pochard, Lesser Scaup, Greater Brazilian Teal

27-28   PHEASANTS: Blue Eared, Brown Eared, Mikado, Impeyan, Tragopans

28   DUCKS: Fulvous Whistling, Janan Whistling, White-faced Whistling, Red-billed Whistling, African Black, Mallard, Hawaiian, Laysan Teal, Florida, New Zealand Brown Teal, Red-crested Pochard, Red-head, Greater Scaup, Mandarin, North American Wood Duck, Black Scater, European Whitewinged Scoter, European Golden-eye, Smew, Hooded Merganser GEESE: Swan, Western Graylag, Eastern Graylag, Western Bean, Russian Bean, Bar-headed, Giant Canada, Atlantic Canada, Moffitt's Canada, Taverner's Canada, Vancouver, Dusky Canada, Cackling Canada, Barnacle, Magpie; Macaws; Parrots; Guinea; Turkey; Peafowl

29   Nene Geese

30   Cranes; Crown Pigeons; DUCKS: Eyton's Whistling, Wandering Whistling, Cuban Tree, Shelduck, Radjah Shelduck, Crested, Bronze-winged, Australian Wood Duck, Comb Duck, Harlequin, Barrow's Golden-eye, Goosander, Red-breasted Merganser;

HATCHING TIME TABLE

DAYS	TYPE OF FOWL
	GEESE: Andean, Ashy-headed, Ruddy-headed, Orinoco, Egyptian; SWANS: Bewick, Whistling
31	Abyssinean Goose; Spotted Whistling Duck
32	Spur-winged Goose, Kelp Goose; Hartbaub's Duck
33	Whooper Swan, Trumpeter Swan
35.	Coscoroba Swan
36	Black-necked Swan, Black Swan
37	Mute Swan
35-40	Rhea
40-42	Ostrich
58-61	Emu

POPULAR FOWL HATCHING CHART

	Days
Chicken	21
Turkey	28
Duck	28
Muscovy duck	33-35
Goose	29-31
Guinea	26-28
Pigeon	16-18
Ring-neck pheasant	23-24
Mongolian pheasant	24-25
Bobwhite quail	23
Japanese quail	17-18
Chukar partridge	22-23
Peafowl	28
Swan	33-37

INCUBATORS

School Project Incubator
5 Egg Capacity

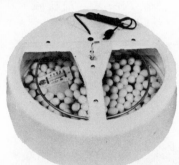

School Project Incubator
70 Egg Capacity

24 Egg Incubator Kit

Marsh Turn-X — 12 Eggs,
24 Quail Egg Capacity.

Turns eggs hourly.
Marsh Roll-X 209 Quail Eggs,
109 Pheasant,
89 Chicken Egg Capacity

Oak Ridge
Automatic
320 Quail Eggs,
100 Chicken
Egg Capacity

Leahy
No. 40
Combination
Incubator
and Brooder

Lyon Transparent Hen*

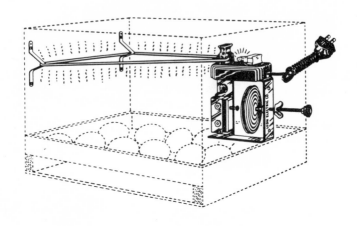

Lyon Make Yourself Incubator Kit — 30 chicken eggs.

*Humidaire
Model 50
700 Quail or
400 Chicken
Egg Capacity*

*Model 14
Humidaire
"Gooser"
300 Goose Eggs*

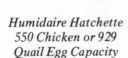

*Humidaire Hatchette
550 Chicken or 929
Quail Egg Capacity*

Petersime

Robbins Hatch-o-Matic

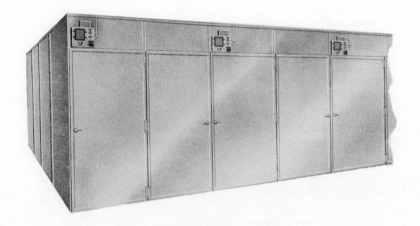

*Multiplo Spacemaster Incubator
of Australia*

Oil Heated Leahy - for remote areas.

CREDITS FOR INFORMATION, CHARTS, PICTURES

Cornell University, Ithica, New York
University of Southern California, Davis, California
University of Missouri, Columbia, Missouri
University of Kentucky, Lexington, Kentucky
Missouri Agricultural Experimental Station, Columbia, Missouri
U.S. Department of Agriculture, Beltesville, Maryland
University of Illinois, Urbana, Illinois
University of California, Berkley, California
University of Lund, Lund, Sweden
California Agricultural Experimental Station, Davis, California
Tennessee Agricultural Experimental Station, Knoxville, Tennessee
Ministry of Agriculture, Middlesex, England
University of Wisconsin, Madison, Wisconsin
Texas A & M University, College Station, Texas
University of Massachusetts, Amherst, Massachusetts
Purdue University, West Lafayette, Indiana
Oregon State University, Corvallis, Oregon 97331
New York Zoological Society, Bronx, New York City
Como Park Zoo, St. Paul, Minnesota
Micky Ollson Bird Farm, Glendale, Arizona
National Zoological Park, Washington, D.C.
Philadelphia Zoological Gardens, Philadelphia, Penn.
San Diego Zoo, San Diego, California

Thank you for your valuable contribution.

GLOSSARY

The following contains terms that are defined in the restricted sense of use in this volume. Many of the words also have other meanings for use in other connections.

ALBUMEN: The white of the egg.

AMNION: A thin protective membrane forming a sac around the embryo.

ANEMIA: A deficiency of red blood cells or of hemoglobin.

ANTIBIOTICS: Substances derived from living organisms which destroy other organism or inhibit their development.

ANTIBODY: A substance in tissue or blood that is specifically antagonistic to a toxin or poison.

ANTIGEN: A suspension of bacterial cells which is used in testing for the presence of antibodies in blood serum.

CHALAZA: A spiral band of thickened albuminous substances in the white of the hen's egg, extending from the chalaziferous layer toward each end of the egg.

CHONDRODYSTROPHY: A condition characterized by shortened extremities and crooked leg bones, resulting from abnormal ossification in cartilage.

CLOACA: The common cavity in birds into which the oviduct, the vasa deferentia, and the urinary and digestive tracts open.

CLUBBED DOWN: Imperfectly emerged down feathers.

CLUTCH: A series of eggs laid on successive days.

CROSSBREEDING: Mating individuals belonging to different breeds or varieties; a form of outbreeding.

DISINFECTANT: A substance that destroys harmful microorganisms.

DUBBING: Trimming of combs or wattles, or both.

EMBRYO: An organism in the early stages of development; a bird prior to hatching.

FERTILIZATION: Union of the sperm and the egg (ovum).

FORMALDEHYDE: A gaseous compound having the chemical formula HCHO; it is a powerful disinfectant having a sharp, penetrating odor.

FORMALIN: A water (aqueous) solution of formaldehyde. The commercial preparation has a strength of 40 per cent formaldehyde.

FUMIGATION: The act of applying a gas, vapor, or smoke as a means of disinfection.

GENE: The basic unit of inheritance in the germ plasm; a hereditary factor.

HORMONE: A chemical secretion from a ductless or endocrine gland which stimulates or inhibits some organ of the body. Hormones are transported by the blood.

INCROSSBREEDING: The crossing of inbred lines of different breeds.

INCROSSING: The crossing of different inbred lines within a breed.

INFUNDIBULUM: The most anterior section, the funnel, of the oviduct.

ISTHMUS: The portion of the oviduct where the egg shell membranes are laid down.

MAGNUM: The section of the oviduct that secretes the major portion of the mass of egg white; it extends from the infundibulum to the isthmus.

NEWCASTLE DISEASE: An acute disease of fowls caused by a filterable virus and characterized by nervous and respiratory symptoms.

OUTBREEDING: The mating of nonrelated individuals.

OUTCROSSING: Mating of unrelated individuals of the same breed or variety.

OVARY: The primary reproductive organ of the female; in domestic fowl normally only the left ovary develops.

OVIDUCT: The tube through which the yolk passes to receive additions of egg white, shell membranes, and shell.

OVIPOSITION: The act of laying an egg.

OVULATION: The release of the ovum from the ovary.

OVUM: A nucleated cell formed in the ovary. In reference to the hen, the term usually applies to the cell product of the ovary along with a much larger mass of nutrients which comprise the yolk of the egg.

PERITONITIS: An acute inflammation of the membrane (peritoneum) that lines the cavity of the abdomen.

SEMEN: Fluid produced in the male reproductive organs that contains the spermatozoa.

SPERMATOZOA: Mature reproductive cells of the male; sperms.

STERILE: Infertile; incapable of reproducing.

THYROID: A ductless, or endocrine, gland in the neck which secretes the hormone thyroxin.

TOM: A male turkey.

UTERUS: The section of the oviduct where the egg shell is formed.

VACCINATION: The protective inoculation with a vaccine for the purpose of increasing the resistance against a specific disease.

VAGINA: The section of the oviduct connecting the uterus and the cloaca.

VITELLINE MEMBRANE: A very thin membrane enclosing the yolk.

YOLK SAC: A more or less sperical sac attached to an embryo and enclosing the food yolk.

DOUBLE CHECK YOUR
THERMOMETER ACCURACY

Your thermometer accuracy is easily checked by comparing it with a fever thermometer. Many hatches have been ruined by unknowingly using a thermometer that is not accurate.

CAUTION — DO NOT SET
BEYOND INCUBATOR CAPACITY

Sometimes there is the temptation to double up, place some extra eggs in your incubator. That is, setting 135 eggs in a 100 egg incubator. This practice can interfere with the proper operation of incubation and hurt your hatches.

CAUTION: ALWAYS
Follow Directions of
Incubator Manufacturer.

REFERENCES

Agricultural Extension of the University of California, ARTIFICIAL IN-SEMINATION OF TURKEYS, Davis, California, October, 1970.

Barott, Herbert George, EFFECT OF TEMPERATURE, HUMIDITY AND OTHER FACTORS ON HATCH OF HEN'S EGGS AND ON ENERGY METABOLISM OF CHICK EMBRYOS, Washington Government Printing Office, U.S.D.A. Technical Bulletin No. 553, 1937.

Bezpa, John, FROM EGG TO CHICK—INCUBATORS AND THEIR OPERATION, College of Agriculture and Environmental Science, Rutgers University.

Briggs, D.M. and J.R. Harris, POLYCHLORINATED BIPHENYLES IN-FLUENCE ON HATCHABILITY, Poultry Science, Vol. LII, No. 5., July, 1973.

Carter, T.C. and B.M. Freeman, THE FERTILITY AND HATCHABILITY OF THE HEN'S EGG, Sumposium No. 5, organized by The British Egg Marketing Board, Edinburgh, 1969.

Cawley, W.O. Dr., FACTORS AFFECTING HATCHABILITY OF CHICKEN EGGS, Texas A & M University, College Station, Texas.

Clemson University cooperating with U.S. Dept. of Agriculture, Prepared by B.L. Hughes, INCUBATING EGGS OF DOMESTIC BIRDS, Circular 530, Clemson, South Carolina, June, 1972.

Cooperative Extension Service, Ohio State University, THE AVIAN EM-BRYO AND RELATED POULTRY SCIENCE PROJECTS, MM-207, Columbus, Ohio.

Cooperative Extension Service, Rutgers University, FIELD STUDIES ON EGGSHELL DAMAGE AND BLOODSPOT DETECTION, Bulletin 403, New Brunswick, New Jersey, July 1972.

Cooperative Extension Service, University of Georgia, FACTORS AF-FECTING SHELL QUALITY, Circular 666, Athens, Georgia, Jan., 1974.

Cooperative Extension Service, University of Illinois, FROM EGG TO CHICK, Circular 878, Feb., 1964.

Division of Agricultural Sciences, University of California, TURKEY BREEDING RESEARCH IN THE WESTERN U.S., Bulletin 830, Davis, California, April, 1967.

Division of Agricultural Sciences, University of California, TURKEY FER-TILITY, Circular 472, Davis, California, January, 1959.

Driggers, James Clyde, PRODUCING HATCHING EGGS IN CAGES BY MEANS OF ARTIFICIAL INSEMINATION, Florida Agricultural Experiment Station, Bulletin No. 551, Oct., 1954.

Fanguy, Roy C., INCUBATION REVIEW, Texas A & M University, College Station, Texas.

Gladish, Gilbert H., A HATCHING GUIDE, Higginsville, Missouri, September, 1956.

Jull, Morley Allan and S. Haynes, SHAPE AND WEIGHT OF EGGS IN RELATION TO THEIR HATCHING QUALITY, U.S.D.A. Journal of Agricultural Research 31(7): 685-694, Oct. 1, 1925.

Ministry of Agriculture, Fisheries and Food, ARTIFICIAL INCUBATION IN SMALL INCUBATORS, Leaflet 341, Edinburgs, May, 1967.

Ministry of Agriculture, Fisheries, and Food, ARTIFICIAL INSEMINATION OF POULTRY, Leaflet 512, Edinburgh, 1973.

Ministry of Agriculture, Fisheries, and Food, GOOSE PRODUCTION, Leaflet 112, Edinburgh, 1972.

Ministry of Agriculture, Fisheries & Food, INCUBATION AND HATCHERY PRACTICE, Bulletin 148, London, Her Majesty's Stationery Office, 1973.

Ministry of Agriculture, Fisheries, and Food, NATURAL HATCHING, Leaflet 43, Edinburgh, 1971.

Ministry of Agriculture, Fisheries, and Food, PHEASANT INCUBATION, Leaflet 145, Edinburgh, 1972.

Poultry Digest, HATCHING EGG MANAGEMENT, Pg, 166-169, Volume 33, Garden State Publishing Co., Sea Isle City, New Jersey, April, 1974.

Silverudd, Martin, SILVERUDD'S MULTIPLE COCK SHIFT SYSTEM, Institute of Genetics, University of Lund, Sweden, 1974.

Skinner, J.L. Dr. and L.C. Arrington, ARTIFICIAL INSEMINATION OF POULTRY, Fact Sheet 31, University of Wisconsin, April, 1969.

Stadelman, William J. Dr. and Owen J. Cotterill, Dr., EGG SCIENCE AND TECHNOLOGY Avi Publishing Co., Inc., Westport, Connecticut, 1973.

Taylor, Lewis W., FERTILITY AND HATCHABILITY OF CHICKEN AND TURKEY EGGS, John Wiley and Sons, Inc. 1949.